'Awe-inspiring and beautifully wri[tten] ailments, aches, and pains and why whole well-being is in our own ha[nds.] Paracetamol packet. Practitioners like Catherine Rolt can help when willing to look under different rocks. I highly recommend this book. It will change your way of thinking about your body and how it works.'

—*Leane Kent*

'This book will draw you in the moment you start to read it. You will not be able to put it down. You will immediately absorb every observation as truth. Once you understand these words of wisdom, an easier and more fulfilling life is assured. This book is essential reading for everyone.'

—*Penelope Karn*

'At a time when Western medicine seeks to impose an unnatural order on our health through a rigid adherence to scientism, one that not only ignores but rejects the natural order, Catherine's new book comes along. *The Pain Paradox* is a timely and welcome reminder of the power, strength, and sheer energy of the natural order. The relaxed style and presentation are a true reflection of that energy, which will encourage readers to re-examine their outlook on life and to celebrate who they really are.'

—*Richard Bellman*

'*The Pain Paradox* will leave you feeling cared for and gently guided to the understanding that there is more right with you than wrong. Pain is not something to be fixed or avoided. Pain is our teacher, leading us on a path of self-discovery that enables us to release the natural forces within our bodies that are the true healers of disease.'

—*Bonnie and David Rowland*

'This book is for you if your condition has taken over your life, and you want to feel better and thrive. *The Pain Paradox* is a unique, accessible, and practical guide full of wit. This is a journey to reconnect with the most extraordinary system for self-healing that we have within. We can be the immediate solution to problems by connecting with the seasons and elements around us, then using the wisdom of our organs and feedback mechanisms. The Pain Paradox will inspire you to be more present and be "better" at living, no matter what.'

—*Alexandra Sagarra*

'Catherine Rolt is a rare breed of practitioner who understands that our most painful trials can turn into our biggest triumphs. She shares her gifts and perspective in *The Pain Paradox*. The ancient medicine described within the pages gets to the heart of pain, meaning the source, instead of sticking yet another plaster on the issue, dealing only with the symptoms.'

—*Denise Stevenson*

the . pain
paradox

How Pain Can Lead to Inner Peace
and Lightness of Being

the · pain
paradox

SUMMIT PRESS
Publishers

CATHERINE ROLT

Printed in the United States of America
First Printing, 2022
ISBN: 9798985054613

Library of Congress Control Number: 2022902991
Summit Press Publishers
411 Walnut Street #12515
Green Cove Springs, FL 32043-3443
author@summit-success.com

Book Layout Quantity sales. Special discounts are available on quantity
purchase by corporations, associations, and others. For details, contact
author@summit-success.com

To my father, David Rolt, who instilled in me an amazing sense of humor. Each day with him was filled with and fueled by emotional intelligence. His passion for his art and his children still leaves me in awe. And to those who find the courage to laugh at life. May this book remind you how much more is right with you than is wrong.

Table of Contents

Introduction

Over the years, people have arrived at my clinic with a list of puzzling maladies that refuse to go away. Many have a long-term condition or chronic disease for which there is currently no cure, one that is managed with drugs and other treatments. Others have a catastrophic condition that has resisted resolution, cancer being the most common. All have a malady of some sort that has all but taken over their life. Among others, these maladies have included:

- Digestive issues
- Sleep disturbances
- Anxiety or depression
- Asthma
- Allergies
- Skin eruptions
- Panic attacks
- Unresolved emotional turmoil
- Auto-immune illnesses

They want relief from this all-consuming issue, maybe even a miracle. Yet they've found traditional medicine profoundly unhelpful for a whole host of reasons—least of which, no one understands their symptoms. They appear to have no physical or pathological cause. Instead, they come from out of left field, or so it seems.

On the one hand, these patients are grateful for the amazing advances modern medicine has made. On the other, they're dismayed by their life's lack of quality and the associated chaos.

Could it all be in their head? They wonder. Maybe they're imagining it all, they say. Why else would they be left with so many unanswered questions, so many inexplicable side effects?

Perhaps like you, they wrestle with illness or pain, knowing damn well that there's more to life than struggle. Half the time, they're on the sidelines of life wondering what hit them; the other half, they feel numb, disconnected from their body.

They spend just a little too much time running around trying to prove they're okay—because we live in a society that rewards positivity, and they're bored with moaning and complaining (though they keep that to themselves as much as humanly possible).

It's exhausting and demoralizing.

They miss carefree days of laughter. They want to be so much more than a sick person.

On good days, when they're not beating themselves up, they instinctively know there's more to this health issue than meets the eye. It's why they sought help that's honest and not so bloody patronizing—why they want a practitioner who's willing to look under different rocks.

On bad days, they see themselves as a hopeless cause. And why wouldn't they? Everywhere they go, they hear what is wrong with them and what they need to fix. They would if only they knew how.

Some of my patients get why they are drawn to me—they sense my compassion for all forms of physical and emotional maladies and offer great relief. That's because I understand chronic pain, disorder, and the associated shame, not just on a professional level, but on a personal one as well.

I grew up with an extraordinary, visceral knowing that if we had been in the animal kingdom, my mother would have eaten me at birth. It would have been a normal response to eat one that appeared to have such a minimal chance of survival. Although my parents didn't know it at the time, I was born with multiple rare genetic disorders that were little understood: Ehlers-Danlos syndrome, mast cell activation syndrome, and postural orthostatic tachycardia syndrome. (Read about them in the reference section if you like.)

I'm now in my sixth decade. So far, my life has been punctuated with well over thirty mostly emergency surgeries, early deafness that was eventually resolved, three different cancer diagnoses, a stroke, multiple "official" labels of diseases or conditions that have had most medics scurrying for the exit door, and more. In other words, my sell-by date, the one my mother no doubt intuited, appears to have been far exceeded.

From a very early age, I experienced one symptom after another, mostly being told that my real problem was hypochondria—that I was attention-seeking, demanding, and/or selfish. Nothing could have been further from the truth, but I did not know that for a very long time.

This lack of understanding from medical professionals and my own family contributed to me feeling generally ashamed and guilty, even polluted. I wanted nothing more than to get my act together, at least at first.

Despite all the twists and turns of my health journey, all the surgeries and interventions, I knew that somehow, I was becoming more alive, passionately engaged, and connected to another layer of all that is integrated in nature. And that I could help others do the same.

Because I know emotional and physical suffering (and know how to thrive, not despite, but because of it) I understand the experiences of my patients. It's why I can give them not just relief, but a whole new lease on life, complete with inner peace, laughter, and lightness of being.

Some of my patients have been referred to me by someone I know—another patient, perhaps, who has experienced a complete transformation. Some have read about a particular type of therapy that falls under the Chinese medicine header—acupuncture, herbal and/or diet, cupping, Shiatsu, and so on—and would like to give it a go seeing as all else has failed. Most are not quite sure what to expect, which has little to do with whether they know me, and more to do with an unfamiliar approach to health.

What is Integrated Chinese Medicine

Integrated Chinese Medicine (ICM) is an ancient medical practice that dates back 5,000 years. It operates under the philosophy that the processes of the human body are interrelated and connected to the environment. Whether we know it or not, our energy systems are constantly interacting with everything around us.

Every single aspect of our lives is about energy, either the movement and flow of it or the stagnation (with its associated consequences). Unexpressed energy sooner or later becomes a block in our guttering systems. The dynamic expression within us, therefore, needs to be given direction if we are to experience relief.

These natural forces within our bodies are the true healer of diseases. They are also the source of symptoms little understood by Western medicine, which views the human body as a composite of separate and somewhat unrelated organs.

When we view the body as an integrated system of mental, physical, and emotional layers, not just a set of isolated parts, we can see the body is communicating with us all the time. We are, after all, an amalgam of body, mind, and spirit, all of which must be examined in terms of energy imbalance. This form of communication, usually overlooked by Western medicine, is invaluable.

Mental, physical, and emotional health are intrinsically linked. Only by treating a patient as a whole person can we tackle the root cause of illness. Dis-ease, as I call it (after all, what is an illness but a lack of ease), is a combination of physical, emotional, and spiritual elements, and should not be considered as being caused by one element in isolation. Living as if each aspect of us is separate as if there are not constant feedback mechanisms pinging between them, is a risky way to go about our business.

The aim of ICM is to connect patients to their bodies, spirits, and minds in an integrated way, to get at that internal guiding system. It will tell us where the imbalance is, allowing the patient to experience a deep inner sense of vitality, which can override any prognosis or appalling set of circumstances.

Such dynamic, energetic health is possible, even when dying.

Health is a Default

Here's the first way the ICM philosophy veers wildly from our Western approach to health: our bodies naturally want to be healthy.

The capacity to unravel dis-ease at its roots is already built into our systems. Our ability to do this unraveling remains intact, no matter how unwell we are. Our systems are built to know and recognize vibrant energetic health. The body, in other words, protects us masterfully and continuously. If we willingly guide it in directions that better adhere to the natural cycles of life—and I'll get to this idea soon enough—then we might experience less resistance, more ease.

The more resistance we have internally, the more we magnetize its external manifestation in some other area of our lives.

What do I mean?

So Within, So Without

This is where the second philosophical difference between the Western medical approach and ICM comes in.

Our days are an unconscious, constant balancing act as we interact with everything and everyone around us, for good or for bad.

Our energy systems resonate either toward vibrant health or toward stagnant, muddied, conflicted frequencies. If we have an internal imbalance or stagnation, it may not disturb only our health; it may also radiate out, starting with how we show up in the world, which then impacts our relationships, which in turn upsets our social network or ecosystem, which impacts society, which spreads to the natural world, the planet.

An imbalance works in the opposite direction as well. An imbalance in the environment can and will affect society, in turn, our relationships, then our health. In other words, energy imbalances are the threads that weave and unwind the entire garment.

If a person has a complaint or symptom, Chinese medicine wants to know how the symptom fits into the patient's entire being and behavior. Illness is situated in the context of a person's life and history—not in a single body part.

Often, a physical manifestation—that lower back pain, skin condition, or digestive problem—is indicative of a relational issue in a patient's life. The physical imbalance aggravates the relationship imbalance, and a cycle is set. Until that cycle gets interrupted, the patient experiences little relief. Back pain, for instance, is the canary in the coal mine that tells us something within a relationship needs to be addressed. A life change needs to be made. The expected fix—by Western standards—often has little to do with what eventually brings the patient back into balance.

Dis-ease is Natural and Useful

The third philosophical difference between Western medicine and ICM may be the most important to grasp.

Dis-ease (and pain) is not there to be fixed or white-washed or run away from. It is not just natural or cyclical; it has a purpose.

You are living in a world that unconsciously promotes the illusion that all suffering can (even should) be eradicated, sorted, or fixed. Ads promoting a painkiller proudly caption "We don't let pain dictate to us."

In other words, they're promoting we don't stop and listen to the profound wisdom of the greatest friend we will ever have—our bodies; that we do not allow it to guide us deeper into the wonderment of our individual paths and skills, even our purpose in this lifetime.

I should add, this profound wisdom is just the start of the journey; it does not mean we have "arrived." We will constantly discover more, particularly through our struggles. Even when there seems to be no hope, there is something more going on, something more to be learned about ourselves and those around us.

Pain is not only the path to self-knowledge but also an ingenious alarm system. Dis-ease is like a car panel that bleeps and lights up to alert us to something vital that needs our attention. We have a series of functions subconsciously operating all the time that naturally respond to the events, people, places, and things outside of ourselves, even those we supposedly have no control over. (You see, the control we think we should have is not the type of control we actually have, not at all.) Sometimes, these responses show up in the form of a dis-ease.

To a large extent, the world ignores, denies, and insidiously punishes pain and dis-ease, adding yet one more dimension to that which we are already contending. We are taught to systematically dismiss and ignore any hint of being out of control, at all costs. Therefore, we continue to live with the rather delicious illusion that we can control ourselves, others, and our lives. When we cannot, well, something must be horribly wrong with us.

Even modern so-called spiritual self-help ignites a sense of guilt and misery when we fail to master our circumstances or rise above pain, overwhelming us with a heightened sense of inadequacy before we even begin the inner journey of self-discovery.

There are several problems with this shame-inspiring belief system, the least of which being it's difficult to find relief when we believe ourselves to be thick-skulled, willful, or broken; we're bent on self-sabotage:

- It is normal to go through levels of dis-ease; it's the human condition. It is part of a constant, fantastic dance with your life force. Our bodies are not static but operate rhythmically from dis-ease back to ease with dis-ease keeping us on the right path to overall health.
- All of life is a perpetual movement through levels of resistance. It's nothing personal.
- Things get worse before they get better. We have so lost touch

with our natural world and its laws that we increasingly fear the real cycles of life.

- Pain (or dis-ease, if you will) is meant to serve as an alarm, to warn us when there's something amiss.
- By going through pain, we become who we are meant to become. Only through each cycle of pain, discomfort, or dis-ease do we master our souls/spirits and our energetic systems—it's how we find our unique path.
- You get better, not by avoiding the cycles of pain, discomfort, and dis-ease, but by going through them.

The Approach

In integrated medicine, we are trained to see, hear, and assess every single detail of a patient's life. The more details we know, in very specific areas, the simpler a diagnosis can become. Every single aspect of how we present ourselves every single day is a loud statement of the state of our organs. (I'll speak to organs throughout, but I'll add here that ICM approaches organs as energy sources as opposed to separate physical forms.)

My job is to:

- Interpret the signs, both proffered and hidden, to help an individual recover their health.
- Seek the root cause of the dysfunction or disease, not just the symptoms.
- Identify the underlying energetic imbalances and disharmony behind an illness.

Assessment starts with an "energetic accounting." Most dis-ease is about one or more of our internal accounts being over or underspent. Our energy—that of our body, mind, and spirit—has its own spreadsheet, which is influenced by any number of things based on our past, present, and future.

Through an energetic balancing process, I help to bring patients home to themselves, to allow them to find ways through the toughest of situations. I help patients connect with themselves and harness all that invariably happens to strengthen, not dwindle, their internal resources.

First, I help them release the shame—because shame stems from the belief that we should never have allowed something bad to happen. Shame feeds suffering. It eats the one who experiences it, then radiates outward, infecting everything and everyone in its path. It sets up an unhealthy relationship cycle, one infused with physical, spiritual, and emotional pain.

This also means that to treat a malady, I may need to look for an energetic imbalance outside of the body because treating dis-ease (which is an energetic imbalance) is why we're here. Restoring health to achieve balance and harmony within or coping with incurable conditions and serious emotional conflicts is the aim.

Our spiritual or emotional health is rarely considered when it comes to dis-ease or chronic illness. Yet dis-ease is often an overriding mechanism that propels the sufferer to return to the scene of unfinished business within.

Current relationships often draw my focus. Dis-ease in many forms is often founded in communications left unspoken—either because we were too afraid, or simply did not know how to express ourselves without creating more issues for us. Relationships of the past can play a major role in a patient's dis-ease. If historical traumas are not first recognized, then released properly and safely, they will find a way out, somehow and in some form. It is never a coincidence when a patient diagnosed with cancer, or another terrifying disease, understands where their energy systems began to be overloaded by events. A patient can, with proper guidance, identify the exact moment when something too shocking or too much to be dealt with in real-time occurred.

A Different Gaze

The fourth philosophical difference between Western medicine and ICM involves how dis-ease is approached, diagnosed, and treated. A Western physician starts with a symptom, then searches for the underlying mechanism, a precise cause for a specific ailment, isolating one single entity. In Chinese medicine, the doctor's gaze is different in that he or she directs attention to the complete physiological and psychological individual. Their gaze is oriented by a whole system based on the cycles of nature. Just as the sun maps out the seasons, so all biological organisms go through predictable changes.

This is where I introduce the five seasons in nature described in traditional Chinese medicine. This is your organizational framework for the book, the very one that informs my patient assessments—many of which I share here. Each of these seasons—autumn, winter, spring, summer, and late summer—has functions and organs associated with it as well as predictable energetic patterns, known as elements. Each of these organs* within your body—most you will recognize, one or two you may not—has its own associated

---

* The organs are not viewed the same way as they are in Western medicine. For instance, the spleen of Chinese medicine is different from the spleen recognized in the West.

emotions. They each have a different form of depression that stems from the organ energy not functioning properly. How they present themselves are covered in corresponding chapters, as they relate to patient cases.

This phenomenal internal system is serving each of us all the time. It is a brilliant warning system, to which we must learn to pay attention. Once we begin the journey of connecting to the functioning of each organ that is working for and on our behalf, on all levels, the simpler it is to master what I call our inner wealth.

Discovering the language of the body—the appropriateness of feelings and how cleverly our bodies respond to reality—allows us to begin trusting our integrated mental, physical, and emotional body. In that, we can begin to feel truly well.

As a practitioner of ICM, the real joy of the clinical work has always been to show people how amazing they are, connecting them to the language of their minds, bodies, and essence (spirit) so that they can enjoy energetic integrated health despite or because of their difficult realities. To thrive, not just to survive.

I intend to show you, too.

Respecting the natural intelligence that is being offered to you all the time, through the language of your body, attuning to it, discovering what your mental, physical, and emotional body is showing you with dis-ease, will allow you to transform your energy. Thriving more dynamically is an automatic result.

It is with simple (though not necessarily easy) changes that you can dramatically experience a difference.

If that's not enough…

In an ever-changing energetic world where seasons, patterns, and rhythms affect us all, you can begin to see how you are also affecting everything around you. The more you get to know the dynamics of your energy/life force, the more alive you feel and the more present you can be to it all.

I.
Autumn/Metal

The Season of
LETTING GO

From my earliest years, my place of solace was nature. Being brought up on an English farm allowed me to soak up the gifts of outside life. My father, who made a living as a painter, was fond of pointing out details—the way the light fell upon a tree, the bluish shadow aside a boulder—things normally unseen to the untrained eye. He had a way of making everything come alive.

Each day, I would walk amongst the animals, in the woods, and across the ever-changing fields that would be harvested at the close of summer. I would absorb how animals interacted with the season, how the rhythms were incorporated into their lives. They showed me how interconnected everything was.

It was nature and her capacity to continually change and grow in cycles that made me realize how extraordinary we all are, how truly internally resilient, as well.

The more I learned to coexist with the earth, the more I discovered nature always has the last word.

Just as a house might be overgrown with ivy seemingly the minute you look away, so your body can be taken over by force if you fail to recognize or respect it.

Much can be gained by watching nature and connecting it with your body. By doing so, you can begin to find your balance.

Autumn brings shorter days and prepares us for winter. In this season, it's time to make sure everything pure and necessary is used and maximized, and that anything unnecessary or wasteful is eliminated.

Just like the autumn season, where the leaves die to make space for new growth in the spring, you need to continually let go of what was or you will get stuck in an unresolved sense of loss with its attendant sadness and grief. The autumn/metal energy within you, if in balance, gives the capacity to take in the richness of life, to feel and move on from losses that are a normal part of life, to accept when something is over, to process and make peace with the loss involved, and then to let go.

The functioning of your organs in the autumn/metal energy within you is deeply connected to your ability to grieve, to take in the richness of life. When you are blocked in your metal element, you simply do not know how to handle grief or transformational change. Suicidal ideation, self-harm, and self-destructive behaviors crop up. You experience a perpetual sense of loss. You appear fragile.

In contrast, when your autumn/metal is in balance, you can enjoy the richness of life, to move on from losses. You have a refinement and quality to your presence. You can efficiently let go of what is not necessary and store only what is needed for winter.

How you are in thought, word, and deed is acutely influenced by what you are taking in and then letting go of via the autumn organs.

Autumn organs include the following:

- Large intestine
- Lungs
- Other autumn associations that inform diagnosis:
- Element—metal
- Emotion/energy—grief and sadness

A balanced autumn provides the ability to:

- Take in the richness of life
- Feel and move on from losses, rather than getting stuck in a perpetual unresolved sense of loss
- Accept when something is over, complete, and that it is imperative to let it go

THE LARGE INTESTINE:
Cut Off

Over the years, many patients have come to my clinics with all sorts of large intestinal tract complaints. They've presented with every possible sign and symptom associated with the large intestine being out of balance, which often includes:

- Abdominal pains
- A sense of fullness
- Diarrhea
- Mucus and blood in stools
- Thirst with no desire to drink
- Burning in the anus
- Sparse, dark urine
- A sense of heavy limbs and body
- Sweating that does not alleviate the fever
- Offensive-smelling stools

In the West, you tend to think of your physical body as just that—a physical shell, nothing more. So, the large intestine, your bowel, is regarded in terms of digestive functioning—namely, bowel movements. Yet, in ICM, the large intestine's function is far more complex. Yes, it allows you to drain the waste that cannot be utilized, but it also allows you to feel and be connected to the world, to take in the richness of life, to accept when something is over. The large intestine gives you the ability to find inspiration and self-respect.

As you let go of your stools, you are endlessly preparing for the continuation of the natural cycle.

A Poor Substitute for Connection

The physical manifestations of an out-of-balance large intestine are not the only symptoms I take note of during an evaluation or energy accounting. They bring patients in the door, certainly, but they are often the least note-worthy manifestations of the dis-ease or imbalance.

Remember when I said that if you have an internal imbalance or stagnation, it may not only disturb your health, it may also radiate out, starting with how you show up in the world, which then impacts your relationships, which in turn upsets your social network or ecosystem, and so on?

Such was the case of the international diamond dealer, who arrived in the clinic one fine day with complaints of loose stools and long-term large intestinal issues.

The woman—I'll call her Fiona—happened to be brilliant in her field. At work, she managed to look tidy; yet, if you were to see her in other settings, which I often did, her appearance was shocking.

Outside of her office, Fiona was unkempt and messy, as if she no longer had any self-respect. She wore a film of sweat, which she carefully masked with make-up during the workday. By five in the evening, her foundation and mascara ran down her face. She had lost almost all her eyelashes, which she knew was the result of rarely taking off her make-up properly, if at all. Like her physical ailments, these were all clues to an energetic imbalance.

In the West, you do not associate loose stools or intestinal issues with the loss of self-respect or changes in hygiene standards.

Nor do you consider that someone's actions may be an attempt to replace the quality of what we call the metal energy.

But in ICM you do.

I will explain.

As a diamond dealer, Fiona traveled in a circle of exquisitely dressed people in the art and high-end interior design world, though she did not fit in well with them. This I surmised was an unconscious attempt on her part to counteract her energetic imbalance.

When you cannot find energy within, you seek it outside of yourself. Fiona's choice of work and friends were an attempt at sustenance. Unfortunately, they served as a poor replacement for her lost metal energy.

Being cut off or disconnected, feeling or acting as if you are inadequate or uninspired, seeking completion and approval from outside of yourself are all indications that your metal is out of balance. The large intestine may be in a weakened state (or the lungs, depending on the symptoms). These were the organs I focused on when treating Fiona.

After treatment (much of which focused on making lifestyle changes), Fiona's personal hygiene altered. Her self-respect improved hugely. She ended up with a varied group of friends, as she did not subconsciously need to replace the metal in her system.

Over the years, it has become more straightforward to key into another's lack of connection to life as it is meant to be lived. If you treat yourself poorly or depend too heavily on a circle of exciting friends to keep you afloat, you may have a metal imbalance rooted in your large intestine. The evidence of an imbalance may be far more obvious than you might guess.

Behavior as a Symptom and a Cure

The more resistance you have internally, the more you magnetize its external manifestation in another area of your life. The very smart, immaculately dressed man who walked into my office one day, barely waiting for the receptionist to let me know he had arrived, was a perfect example. It was not difficult to conclude that he was driven, overworked, and an overachiever in all areas of his life. That impatience was his middle name.

Gerard, as I will call him, sharply assessed my treatment room to determine if it was clean enough for him to sit down and if, indeed, I was someone with whom to spend his precious time. He was unyielding and totally commanding. You might say he had an overabundance of metal.

Mostly bored with his life, Gerard was used to being intimidating without fully being aware it pushed away the very thing he longed for—connection. Perhaps this was the source of the depression for which he was seeking treatment. We both knew he had only come out of idle curiosity. He didn't expect any real help.

Lucky for him, I had been brought up around many similar characters, so Gerard was familiar to me. (For what it's worth, my mother's people had roses named after them, claimed members of royalty as godparents.) Feeling inadequate and empty, not unlike the diamond dealer, this man was the sort who sought a sense of wealth and richness outside of himself.

Living life as if the external is the top priority leads to a collective feeling of internal bankruptcy. This was true for Gerard, as is the case for many in our society. Try as he might, I wasn't intimidated; I was, however, tired.

At seven in the evening, it had already been a long day. Despite my fatigue, it was too late to cancel the appointment. Instead, I asked if he would join me for a cup of tea. I was deliberately offering him a connection. He nonchalantly said that he would.

How you respond to another is a display of how energetically balanced your organs are.

Sometimes, a metal imbalance can be like having a giant disposal unit where, no matter how delicious and lovingly prepared the food is, the whole lot goes down practically unseen, unappreciated, certainly not connected to, and trashed.

When you are disconnected from your inner wealth, meeting a friend in a restaurant can result in a performance/drama, as the table setting, placement of the chairs, where the door is located, anything and everything will be a constant reason to avoid settling in or otherwise connecting with what is in front of you. Such was the case with Gerard, who couldn't be pleased with the chair he sat in.

The metal/autumn energy out of balance can become apparent in a person constantly having a glass-half-empty mentality; for example, someone has millions in assets but, submerged in the energetic experience of poverty, can only see the oppressive size of the tax bill.

Gerard's energy was longing for quality which he could not find within himself. I was connecting immediately to that for him.

Gathering myself long enough to boil a kettle and properly lay the tray, I reminded myself that I was able to be beside this man as he unraveled what was eating away at him. I could be with him and truly listen.

As we are not taught to listen to each other effectively, we often overlay each other's conversations with our noise and needs. In other words, the connections that you so long for may be missed entirely due to your inability to truly hear another.

When you are far less noisy in your being, when you are not running from your pain, you can pick up the endless cues to have meaningful connections, rather than being cut off or aloof.

"I do not believe you can help me, but as you have come highly recommended, I thought I would at least come and meet you," he began.

The "highly recommended" had appealed to his internal discon-nection to his quality and was yet another clue to the state of this man's energy.

That was the beginning of what ended up being a very enjoyable two-and-a-half hours. As I understood the energy of the organs and where he was so stuck and struggling, I felt huge compassion for his cut-off state.

After I had finished, instead of adjusting his diet or giving him a course of acupuncture, I chose an unusual treatment for him. First, I made taking him on as a patient conditional, which surprised him to no end. He was not accustomed to being refused. Second, I assigned him odd homework.

"Each week for the next three weeks, I want you to find three people to whom you can make a significant difference financially. By the way, lump sums rarely work as they are not getting involved enough with the root causes of another's financial lack. So, you are going to have to use your genius to make a real and lasting difference to nine separate individuals."

His eyebrows shot up; his bewilderment turned to shock. He awakened and gave me his total concentration.

I continued, "You have to do so anonymously. You need to find ways of discovering those under your very nose who are struggling financially."

I explained that he was so wealthy in terms of finances, but starving for connections and internal wealth, leaving him a barren wasteland on the inside—and that was at the heart of his malaise, the one for which he sought treatment.

Three weeks later, Gerard returned beaming with a totally transformed energy. He bounded into the treatment room like a buoyant teenager. His cut-off and exacting energy had dispersed.

He went on to explain that he had no idea what a difference he could make to the lives of others, that he adored the challenge of bothering with those right under his nose—that acting anonymously was glorious.

"No one understands what on earth has come over me. I'm even reviewing my friends rather differently. All the agitation, sense of listlessness, and boredom have disappeared."

Release

Westerners, particularly the British, are clogged up by our inability to express grief; in turn, we are incapable of experiencing joy (the paradox that is life).

Letting go can create joy.

The large intestine helps you continually transform what you take in and let go of. Once you fully absorb the fact that you are going to be on a voyage of letting go all the time, you can get on with embracing what you take in. You can begin to see that every single one of us is struggling with sadness and grief. Giving yourself to others is often the best way to give to yourself, to strengthen your energy.

THE LUNGS:
Grief

From a very early age, I learned to hide my physical and emotional pain. My digestion was not working. Gynecologically, I was in trouble, so I had been placed on birth control pills at the age of eleven. A couple of years later, the collagen in my body lost its ability to operate. Tennis, riding, running, fencing, tap dancing—even Russian dancing, which had been one of my party tricks—came to an abrupt halt as I was carted off to the hospital to receive eleven weeks of traction.

All types of movement had been my solace; so, for me to collapse and be removed from my friends one day and put into the hospital the next came as a devastating shock. I never returned to school and was put to bed for a year of treatments.

During my time in the hospital, I thought I was going to die. I was rather disappointed that I did not. I had no way of understanding that I was grieving deeply all that I loved; to me, it was a death.

It was also deeply confusing to have something wrong with me that was not based on my growing character flaws, as reported to me by various family members (my mother, in particular). What I was taking in was not very palatable.

The lack of understanding from medical professionals and my family also contributed to my feeling of being messy and polluted in general. My focus shifted to "getting my act together," rather than experiencing all that I lost.

As the years went on and I grew into a young woman, aspects of my behavior changed as my self-respect and self-worth improved. I learned to stop bullying myself, which then stopped telegraphing the subtle invitation to do the same to the outside world. I built up my metal.

I tell you this story because I am living proof—as you breathe in and let go in the cycles of life, you can more deeply connect into a more wakeful, conscious state. You can experience loss, then let it go, without getting stuck. And that's where your lungs come in.

What I Look For

The emotion associated with the lungs is grief, so if you are in balance, within your energy, you will be able to grieve appropriately. In other words, you will be able to allow your mind, body, and spirit to continue the process of living while simultaneously grieving your losses. You will be able to respond to sad events in ways that keep your energy moving.

The sound associated with the lungs is weeping, which an experienced practitioner will be able to detect in the tones of your voice if your lungs (or large intestine)—parts of your metal element—are out of balance.

Other signs and symptoms of an imbalance include:

- Shortness of breath
- A weak and hoarse voice
- Frequent colds
- Fatigue

- Watery sputum
- A pale, white complexion
- Spontaneous daytime sweating
- Dry coughs or dry mouth and throat
- A dislike of speaking
- Body aches with a runny nose
- Stuffiness in the chest
- Loose stools
- Seemingly inappropriate grief
- Malar flush
- Occipital headaches
- Poor appetite
- Wheezing
- A feeling of being clogged up
- Heaviness
- Fuzziness or dizziness of the head

In the grief recovery process, which I helped bring to the UK, you learn to recover from, not forget, all sorts of losses. It is so incredibly sad to hear so many people talk about "never being able to recover" from a loss, because in believing that, they unknowingly seal their ill-health fate.

What Grief Looks and Sounds Like

Very early on in my practice, I had the privilege of meeting an extraordinary woman I will call Felicity. By the skin of my very inexperienced teeth, I managed to look beyond her outer appearance and see her brilliance and inner wealth. That first appearance could easily have disguised the gem that she was.

I had been called to do a home visit. The smell, as she opened her door, hit me full in the face; I almost gagged. It was the stench of waste and cats—which were living in almost every spot that was not cluttered.

Everywhere I looked was a mess. Felicity had piles and piles of things that she was working on, seemingly all at once. This consisted of the most precious of silk rugs with the occasional dress design for a wealthy Indian princess. Felicity was a textile artist of great repute.

Felicity's body mass fell off her in huge folds, as if somehow disconnected. Between the folds, she had developed sores, some of which were infected. She was so ill, hardly able to breathe or move around.

And yet, when I looked at the quality of her work, it was exquisite. The dresses she produced were of the finest material and could not have been more perfectly made. The two versions of Felicity did not coincide.

When I asked Felicity a host of questions, it was easy to see how disconnected she was from her talents, her inner and very refined wealth. It was as if she had so much grief, she was almost dying. She was stuck in an everlasting autumn energy that was now totally out of balance.

The worse her sense of inner poverty, disconnection, and grief had become, the more trapped she was in her rotting skin.

For six weeks I treated her intensively in her home, two, sometimes three times weekly, until she was well enough to come to the clinic. The intention of the clinical and integrated medicine was to let her body find its way through the stacked, stuck, rotting autumn energy—to invite her body to find its inner wealth again so that she could connect to, then begin to take care of, herself.

During the course of our treatment, she talked about all the dreadful losses in her life. The death of her brother, whom she adored, when she was thirteen. With her brother's death, she had also lost her parents, as they did not know how to recover from the loss.

I witnessed the intense realities of these losses, showing her how vital it was for her to allow herself to grieve, to let go when crying, which was her body's way of releasing the pain.

It was easy to show her the deep respect that I felt. First, because it was astounding to me that she was able to function at all. Second, because she was so highly acclaimed, despite her sad past.

When I asked her about her fame, the weeping noise and tone of her voice would become more pronounced. She became more distressed, then cut off.

I gave her homework that would help her build connection, a sense of being complete, to find meaning again. She was to work one evening a week as a volunteer with disabled children, teaching them quilting, which was healing for her.

To become healthier, happier, and more peaceful, we must serve one another. By serving others, you serve yourself.

During this time, Felicity lost about two stone (twenty-eight pounds), her skin began to heal, and her eyes shone. Her hair, which had hung limp and dirty around her face, came back to life. She even began to tidy up the mess in which she lived. Felicity began to arrive at the clinic as the relatively young and still very attractive woman that she was.

Within weeks, she was commissioned to work on a very famous tapestry in France, which meant trips to a glorious Chateau. She was finally able to take in the wealth of her talents.

One evening, nine months later, I attended a party at her home. As I walked in, I was met by a lovely, smiling waiter in a crisp black and white uniform. The house, like Felicity, was unrecognizable. It was smart and tidy; flowers were everywhere; the clutter was gone. All was in its place. There seemed to be only one rather regal-looking cat wandering about.

The radiant, now slim, patient stood in her drawing room holding court, her head tipped back as she released a stream of rich laughter. She was radiating her inner wealth. Her metal energy had been reclaimed as she had let go of her stored-up grief.

When your lungs are functioning at an optimum energetic level, you can finally take in the richness of life.

Remembering With Pleasure and Joy

A client I'll call Burton came to see me for some grief recovery work. He was very self-aware and knew that he could not go into his future successfully in his present state of "stuck-ness." He had two children who, although young adults, needed him to be present to their needs as well.

"My wife," Burton said, "would not want me to be living half-heartedly until I see her again."

He explained that he had been widowed relatively young and had promised his wife that he would not let grief take over, yet he had underestimated the reality of her death.

So, we carefully laid the foundation for Burton to energetically move beyond the current pain cycles. They were not going to stop until his body, spirit, and mind had spat out what needed to be witnessed, acknowledged, and healed.

The time came, which was very momentous for Burton, to read aloud a letter he had written intending to release the emotional charge in his pain.

Twisted in a physical ball of wretchedness, he began. As he read, tears poured down his face, his body shook, and his coloring changed. When Burton finished, he sighed and went slightly limp; the briefest of smiles appeared on his face.

I said nothing, allowing the silence to descend like a glorious first coating of snow.

After several minutes of comfortable silence, we both heard a loud grunting below the treatment room.

"Is that what I think it is?" he asked.

"Yup, I think it really is. A new tenant moved in just this week."

Clearly, a woman in the throes of total bliss and passion was beginning to grunt, then shout, as an all-embracing orgasm flooded her body.

Burton and I looked at each other and roared with laughter.

"My wife would have loved that timing!"

He felt totally different. Burton could sense life beckoning him, though he wasn't convinced he was up for another woman, yet.

Did it mean that he wouldn't feel sad again? Of course not. But a shift in the season within him had returned Burton to remembering his wife with pleasure and joy.

When in Hell, Keep Going

You must continually find your balance within the ebb and flow of events. Shit will continue to happen. Society permits the so-called "positive" emotions but has this constant resistance to what is perceived as "negative"—certainly not allowing for the honest, normal human experience of grief and pain.

From an early age, you are taught to hide at least half of what is happening routinely to you. And yet, you must work through it, or you never get beyond.

II.
Winter/Water

The Season of
EXERTING YOUR WILL

Winter, the cold and dark season, is a time of inward reflection, rest, and restoration; of building your reserves and cherishing your resources; a time to slow down and feed yourself both physically and spiritually. Winter is about storing up potential and using your resources wisely. It is this concentrated and internal force of winter that enables a seed to burst forth in spring growth.

In ICM, winter is associated with water, the element of pooling, tranquility, and flow. Peaceful imagery aside, water always gets its way eventually. As a respected teacher once said, "Over time, it will erode the toughest materials on this planet, so never under- or overestimate the water, the will within people. The excess, hindrance, or lack of water equally will cause total and absolute devastation if left to its relentless ways."

There is depth, darkness, and mystery to winter/water. When misspent, this forceful element can lead you to overuse your will, which leads to deep-seated exhaustion and burnout. In nature, groundwater is like your savings account. It's okay to draw it down when you need it, but if it's not replenished, eventually it will be gone. Then you're left bankrupt.

The emotion associated with the winter/water element is fear. In appropriate amounts, fear is essential to survival because it enables you to navigate situations with care and caution.

When your winter/water energy is balanced within your clever body, you notice danger and assess the risk that something—or even someone—presents. Like an animal that seeks refuge on higher ground before huge natural disasters or a mother who knows when her children are in danger even though she may be far from them at the time, your life force can clue you into danger. You will be able to take action to protect yourself.

When the winter/water element is out of balance, you might experience excess fear, phobias, and lack of courage. An overly anxious mind does not accurately assess situations or easily grasp the consequences created when living with the effects of a revved-up engine or system. It also becomes tricky to identify when you are underestimating or overestimating a situation, which may cause you to skirt the truth to ward off something (or someone) scary. You will lie, giving others information you think they want to hear, which can overtax your system.

Like water, the truth will always have its way. The truth always comes out and usually in a torrent of water-like eruptions that shock everyone. These unexpressed thoughts and feelings are often the underlying cause of dis-ease in many forms.

On the other end of the spectrum, an imbalance of the winter/water energy may present as a lack of fear, which can lead us to underestimate the dangers, again nearly to the point of being unwise. Such a lack of balance can lead to very subtle and controlling behavior simply because of such anxiety. A person may exhaust himself with the perceived danger of every possible event. Such a person may feel unsafe so often that safety is sought in outward control, when in fact it is the inward lack of safety that must be resolved.

One of the amazing things about becoming aware of your winter/water element is that you become much more conscious of what you are asking of yourself and, therefore, of others. Only then will you stop burdening others with your carelessness or lack of discernment, thereby dwindling yours and their internal resources.

One of your body's brilliant alert systems is your ability to experience fear at differing levels, and the organs associated with winter/water are partially responsible for this ability.

Winter organs include the following:

- Bladder
- Kidneys

Other winter associations that inform diagnosis:

- Element—water
- Emotion/energy—fear/anxiety

A *balanced* winter provides the ability to:

- Notice danger, assessing the extent of risk being presented
- Take action to deal with risks in appropriate ways
- Provide reassurance about safety

THE BLADDER:
Appropriate Fear

Chances are good you know at least one person who is so caught up in people-pleasing she (and this could just as easily be a he) takes on the burdens no one else can be bothered to carry. She is reluctant to disagree with others even if she's dead right. She seems to have little will. This is a sign that she is likely off-balance in her winter/water element.

Communication skills are often rooted in real and underlying anxiety of how you will be judged—thus, the reluctance to push back against others when you should.

Take the stunningly elegant woman who walked into my clinic one day, sat down, then slumped over my consulting table. Her terror hung like a thick fog in the room. "Please, I beg you," she wailed, "listen to me, just listen to me. I'm desperate and I need your help."

I told her that I would do just that and not interrupt until she had finished. "Tell me, please, I want to hear and listen."

Grace looked into my eyes to see if I was for real. An internal flood seemed to roar through her. "You see, I know that I'm dying. I so passionately don't want to die." On she babbled like a brook.

She went on to explain that she had two adopted children and a husband whom she adored. She was terrified by what her death would do to them all. "I have been scanned twice and three consultants and four radiologists say they cannot see anything wrong.

Therefore, all my symptoms are coming from early menopause and hysteria. I know with everything in me that they are wrong."

I shook my head. As a practitioner, I have worked with hundreds who have experienced the worst of what can and does happen in a lost and broken medical system. They have been scapegoated and treated appallingly, given rude assessments, which only arrogance might justify. They have been burdened with the belief that the sign, symptom, or pain of which they complain is not real and that perhaps they are mad or neurotic.

As the patient, I have seen this up close as well.

Thanks to these very rare genetic syndromes that I was born with, ones that few understand, I have bumped up against the limits of the Western medical system my entire life, respecting what is to be respected and leaving the rest alone as far as is possible. It has been like walking through a minefield where I try not to trip up the fragile egos or arrogance that buffer fear. When I must put up a fight, however, I will. Grace was unable to do that.

"I know I have a brain tumor," she said, with total certainty. "Why will they not believe me? Why won't they question their machines? You have to believe me. I'm dying and I don't have long left."

Caught in the headlights, this Bambi-like creature appealed to every bit of me to believe her.

And I did.

"Will you let me take your pulses?" I asked. I went to her when she nodded, again deep in her turmoil of very appropriate terror. I held her hands and took all twelve of her pulses. Sure enough, out of several blocks that we can feel that indicate death, she had all of them. Her fear, in other words, was well-founded. Her water energy was alerting her, loud and clear.

"I believe you."

She sat up—validated, reassured. She certainly was not crazy.

"I hear you and I totally believe you, which I will keep validating for you. The big question is this: Since you are dying and there may not be anything anyone can do, are you willing to come to terms with what you do have right now—and not waste a remaining minute?"

She snapped out of the state of terror which, frankly, I had prayed might happen. She needed to use what life force she had left to put her affairs in order.

We talked of her need to make plans and to prepare her husband and children. I encouraged her to go back to the hospital and demand they rescan her that day.

I shall never forget the dignity and grace with which she walked out of the clinic room.

Her husband rang me that night to thank me. They had rescanned her and found a tumor that was already so huge, they could not understand how it could have been missed before. They were appalled, not that they had missed the tumor, but that she had driven herself to the hospital.

When the time came, as it did some six weeks later, she was very much at the helm; her family was at peace.

Balance

You're often told that your fear is unjustified, that you are making mountains out of molehills, particularly when you exert your will. Yet the bladder is incredibly clever. The bladder is associated with wisdom that compels you to expend your willfulness and resources or to withdraw from a situation that compromises you. It helps you know when to correct an under- or overuse of your will.

Fear, the emotion that is governed by the bladder, needs to be expressed in genuine proportion to what is happening. It should not be overblown or absent, neither of which is healthy.

A healthy functioning bladder keeps your life force, your energy, in check.

An energetic imbalance in the bladder can look like many things.

On a physical level, bladder syndromes primarily revolve around what we call damp heat or damp cold in the bladder, which often presents as difficult, burning, turbid, painful, frequent, or urgent urination.

Other physical symptoms include:

- Lower back pain
- Knee issues
- Sacral, hamstring, calf, or Achilles pain
- Weakness of hearing and vision
- Fertility issues
- Weakness in teeth and hair loss

Apart from uncovering an excess exposure to cold, damp, or heat, I would also establish if you were having too much sex, an element of your full energetic picture. (All jokes aside, some people fill their emptiness with excess sex—excess in terms of what your body can successfully process. This is not a moral judgment.)

Long-term, unresolved emotional problems are always something I would be looking at with this element as well.

A Dangerous Lack of Fear

You may recall, on the other end of the spectrum, an imbalance of the winter/water energy may present as a lack of fear, which carries with it several problems that play out in your interaction with others.

The Colonel, as I will call him, was most put out by frequent and urgent urination, feeling thirsty but not wanting to drink anything. He had blood in his urine and still would not go to his doctor, whom he called an idiot. He had come to me only because one of his batsmen had given him acupuncture during the war, so he had faith in the art.

The Colonel was an incredibly charismatic but disturbingly unpleasant man (if you can imagine the combination).

Back in his heyday, he had been awarded high honors and awards for heroism, which he took seriously indeed. Because he was lauded for outstanding bravery, he believed that he was untouchable. From his perspective, he was above the law. He could do precisely what he wanted when he wanted. Such was his unfettered will.

For some, controlling behavior is likely a symptom of an imbalance in the water, bladder energy, simply because of the anxiety going on all the time. A person can exhaust himself with perceived fears and dangers. Feeling unsafe, this type will seek safety in outward control, when in fact the inward lack of safety is what needs to be resolved. But this unpleasant man, who went out of his way to bait my staff—for fun and malice, I suspect—was out of balance because he had an arrogant lack of fear.

This lack of fear made being in The Colonel's presence tantamount to being trapped in a cage with a lion. At any moment, he might pounce. He wanted to make mincemeat of me before he'd even walked through the treatment room.

I knew in my bones that he was a sexual predator, trapping women and, I suspect, men, in his dreadful, manipulative ways. He was that polluted.

I'd been in clinical practice for quite some time, so I was able to handle him in ways that worked for me and did not leave me crushed by the force of his "waters." I was also sufficiently in balance myself to assess the dangers properly. Treating him was not just in service to him, but the world at large.

Often during treatment, he would put his slightly reptilian eyes on me and ask me deliberately inappropriate questions. He was only interested in me personally and sexually as he was convinced that he could change my mind. No for him was just the beginning of the conversation; he knew he had his prey where he needed them to be. He had a putrid smell, which no amount of heavy cologne would cover. Remaining consciously meticulous in my professional conduct and manners, I treated what I was able to treat and allowed him to become sufficiently bored by the total lack of a game or a chase. I kept command.

With treatment, some of the very nasty baiting improved. (His baiting became less pointed and happened less often.)

Years after I treated him, I saw an article about him written by a very brave journalist who questioned the motives of his so-called bravery. Having interviewed him very perceptively, he had glimpsed what was really going on with this national hero.

Get Help

If you are beginning to realize that you have (or someone you love has) a total disregard for the safety of you or others—if danger is a huge turn-on—you may want to go directly to your nearest and best ICM practitioner and have him or her begin to put you back in balance, for your sake and the sake of others.

THE KIDNEYS:
Denial

Rose had not originally come to resolve her domestic situation; she was, in fact, unaware that it was at the root of her debilitating condition.

Instead, Rose had presented with the following symptoms, common to kidney issues:

- A sore and aching back that worsened at night
- A dry throat and mouth at night
- Night sweats
- Tinnitus
- Constipation with dry stools interspersed with loose stools, seemingly out of the blue
- The beginning of edema in her legs
- Knees that were cold to touch, weak, and painful
- A blue tint under her eyes and around her mouth
- Swelling of the legs

It was the trouble with her legs that had driven Rose to seek treatment. Going out publicly to very grand affairs with her high-profile husband, who peacocked around with her, had become unnerving because she now had to hide her legs, which he considered to be her best feature. This insecurity had caused her husband to become crueler and far more controlling.

One day during treatment, Rose finally felt safe enough to spit out what I had known to be her real issue. Her pulses, coloring, and voice had been telling me that something was seriously amiss. She had a groan that bubbled on relentlessly, creaking under the weight of her water.

"I now realize I am being raped every night. My husband never asks. He will even barge into my bathroom if he decides he wants his fix. I'm his property, as is everything else." She babbled the statement so quickly I could easily have missed it. "I hadn't realized that 'no' does not exist in my world with him. I'm beginning to see the terrible danger I'm in, particularly now that I want to protect myself and take action."

Even before she said as much, it was clear to me that she was being violated every single day and in every possible way. I understood Rose better than she did herself.

When I was young, no one knew that I had experienced sexual abuse at the hands of one of the medics entrusted with my care. I was fully developed as a woman but ill-prepared to pay the price it extracted. I had no haven from which to learn how to defend myself or how to behave, given that I appeared to be a walking piece of meat. The irony is, that experience turned me into a deep listener, someone you can tell your deepest secrets, fears, and worries to because I understand hidden pain.

I admired Rose for turning up to see me at all, and so resolutely. The kidneys, like the bladder, the center of your winter/water energy, provide you with your will. For Rose, it was functioning at least that well. For what was going on inside of her, she was quite intimidating. She came across as having her act together. Rose was so in control of everything, she appeared calm. Yet, I was able to see, feel, and sense her underlying agitation. I knew Rose was in grave danger, so I had to contain my real and appropriate fear for her.

I had been waiting for her energy to build back up so she would have the strength to come to terms with her truth, and then face her situation, which would get worse before it got better. (Such is the case with much of healing.)

The truth was, as frightening as Rose's situation was, she was more afraid of venturing into the unknown, of becoming an outcast in her social circle. Her husband, she knew, would manipulate what remained of her family, many of whom had colluded with childhood abuse.

The first step was to put safety precautions in place for Rose. We used stealth, discretion, and careful planning to work around her reality as, step-by-step, she decided what she wanted to do.

The second step was returning to the scene of the crime, her childhood abuse. Only then would Rose be able to heal and release herself.

The familiar must never be underestimated; it will always serve as a comforting beacon, no matter how dangerous, or seemingly outrageous, or confusing it is to others. The familiar will propel you to return to the scene of unfinished business within.

Rose was familiar with violence, thanks to her childhood. It was still alive and vibrating in her body. Subconsciously, she was an open wound energetically emitting a frequency for another damaged abuser to come along. She had been drawn to the familiar, and, complicated by a major imbalance in her kidney energy, she had not recognized the danger. Her husband had smelled familiar to her, so she mistakenly thought she was going home.

How clever our bodies are! They will keep magnetizing the very things that need to be resolved—in their greater wisdom and energetic truth, they act as a constant antenna to the higher possibilities of vibrant integrated health.

Eventually, Rose took the leap and rescued herself, after a long, drawn-out process that involved not getting caught by her cruel husband due to the obvious shift in her energy.

Into Me I See

Like Rose, Edgar had come to my clinic to address a presenting problem that was merely the tip of the iceberg.

"My teeth are all beginning to wobble and I'm getting fewer erections which are somewhat flaccid."

As I worked through my assessment, a powerful quote that I had come across in my studies came to mind. It summed up the character in front of me: The art of seduction can impede all forms of real and safe intimacy.

Intimacy is about knowing the truth of oneself, then allowing others to know it too. This man was doing everything in his power to avoid self-knowledge. And running away from his truth was costing him.

Edgar was a sex addict, though he would not say as much. All his relationships were in shreds, which he believed had to do with "them," not with his behavior. He had learned to be very seductive and charismatic in his intense desire and need to get what his body demanded. His body chemistry was now running his vehicle.

Survival mechanisms tend to have a short shelf life. They start with behavior that seems reliable, until suddenly it fails. Quick fix sex was no longer giving him the charge that he was after.

Danger was knocking at Edgar's door on many integrated levels. He could not detect it as he was so caught up in the vicious cycle of desperate energetic, physical, chemical, mental, and emotional turmoil. He was blind to his truth.

I was very familiar with addictions. I recognized the signs of someone being driven by a relentless inferno, which no amount of sexual release was going to quench. His pulses demonstrated that every single time he was having a momentary sexual release, he had further emptied his precious resources, which was making the problem worse.

The fact that his hearing was going or that his memory was beginning to fail did not seem to alarm him at all. He was in no way picking up on any of the feedback mechanisms that his body was giving him.

If asked, he would have told you that the profound noise in his head and the burning heat in his groin was not noticeable on the outside. All the time wondering how he could get his next sexual fix.

He was paying a huge bill for his burnt-out system.

Beyond his compulsion, he worked in a competitive environment where he was encouraged to play hard. He used cocaine and alcohol as a normal part of his days, which were continually long and over-adrenalized.

He was so out of balance that it did not occur to him to get anything fixed, apart from what he thought was "fixing" him seven to ten times a day.

Without a shift, he was in danger of a stroke or heart attack. Within his energy bank, he had spent his one-time inheritance; he was bankrupt. His water tank was empty.

No wonder his erections were "flaccid."

Knowing that patients who do not know themselves well will not answer questions accurately, it is up to the practitioner to be a good detective so that the truth can be assessed. The backing of the body's clever language speaks loudly to us. You must follow those signals to provide proper treatment. You must cleverly work around a mind that does not want to be known.

After several visits, I asked Edgar if he was interested in learning about how to rebuild his energy through the mastery of his sexual desires. After initial resistance, eventually, he learned to master his sexual energy and replenish his internal resources to some degree. As his energy grew, he became aware of his warning light system.

A year later, he walked into my clinic and reported that he had resigned from his job, and it was the best decision of his life. He also had very clear plans of what he was going to do; taking into consideration his integrated needs, he no longer ran by desperation.

He was even learning to be intimate with one woman and allowing himself the support of a therapist.

"I'm not sure I can believe it myself, but I'm enjoying being faithful and not cricking my neck every time a skirt goes past."

Avoidance Has a Cost

If you can tune in to what's going on inside of you, pinpoint the source of energetic imbalance and discomfort, you can understand how it affects everything else, everyone else. But to get at any of that, you need to know yourself first—and in this noisy world, that takes some doing. Addictions not only keep you blind to your truth, but they also bankrupt your energy supplies. The depletion of your resources leads to more anxiety and long-term, unresolved emotional problems.

III.
Spring/Wood

The Season of
BENDING WITH THE WIND

In the spring, everything blooms. Put a seed in the ground, and even if you forget it, it will often fight its way through the resistance of all that surrounds it to push its way out of the dirt. A seedling will find its way out from seemingly impossible constraints.

In traditional Chinese medicine, all of life is perpetual movement through levels of resistance; there is nothing personal about it. This is what the spring/wood energy is all about. Healthy bamboo is rooted, empty, and flexible. It can bend completely backward in the wind without snapping in two. Its strength lies in going with the winds while not getting diverted from its direction of growth, which is its healthy internal inclination.

This is a metaphor for life. Truly peaceful living is attained by practicing being empty, detaching yourself from all that you are, to become who you are meant to be, regardless of how painful the process.

Regardless of the obstacles, you, too, can spring forth after long winter hibernation. You may have thought that you would never be able to resurrect from the darkness and silence of the previous season—the short days, the sense that all has died—yet you do. In the spring, your body propels you forward, often right into essential decisions you must make.

Spring is the time for you to reach outward and develop deeper roots. Roots must emerge and follow their growth path, straight through concrete, if need be, and so must you. The obstacles and frustrations you encounter are inherent to the spring energy. By learning to befriend the natural layers of frustration, you can discover yourself. Your spring/wood energy can allow for a gentle acceptance of even the most unacceptable. The painful cutting back of seemingly everything can strengthen you.

Over time, I understood that our bodies give an automatic sense of drive and purpose. Each time another roadblock rises in front of me, or another part of me will not physically work in the way I want, I find myself diverting, driving to find another way. I assert myself in ways that I would have never thought possible. Like that tree root, my days become an experience of how much more I can become.

Bamboo does not take the wind's whistle, rage, or force personally. If you often do, it may be a sign of imbalance. When you fight against obstacles and your true nature, you heap stress onto your clever system. Your system is designed to become increasingly empty or still from the middle out, and then unattached yet rooted, so you can continue to develop your potential through the endless storms with which you must contend.

The spring/wood energy gives you the capacity to find your unique path. When in balance, it is about developing yourself. As your sense of self develops, your connection to your maturity, spirituality, and sexuality grows. Everything becomes a little frisky, mischievous, and expansive as the spring sap rises. Your energy seems to become richer and more profound. You cease taking anything too seriously (except when you do, of course, and land in a heap of intensity).

When your spring/wood energy is stuck and stagnant, you can veer between apathy and rigidity, defiance, and the tendency to seek justice beyond your boundaries. Not everything, by the way, is yours to deal with.

Anger is the emotion associated with spring/wood energy. All the emotions, but particularly anger, are so often misunderstood. Anger is an energy frequency we all need.

It is vital to unpack this anger, which is often at the root of dis-ease. Without the energy of appropriate anger, you can get trapped. Anger and frustration can control you, leaving no one in charge of your dynamic life force, which includes this anger. (When used wisely and channeled into appropriate levels of assertion, anger is paramount to your evolution and growth.)

When you constantly take frustrations and obstacles personally and react out of frustration and anger, the internal wind starts to build in your system, often leading to strokes and heart attacks. Like a wind that can suddenly stir the waters and wreak havoc in nature, your behavior can become unpredictable, rapid, and erratic. You can become belligerent or, on the other end of the spectrum, overly timid, both of which impede your personal growth.

The spring organs allow the free flow of emotional states; they are the conductors of all your emotions. As such, they must be brought into balance.

Spring organs include the following:

- Gallbladder
- Liver

Other spring associations that inform diagnosis:

- Element—wood

- Emotion/energy—anger/frustration

A balanced spring provides the ability to:

- Assert yourself appropriately in the world
- Have structures and boundaries so that the path can unfold
- Make plans and decisions
- Have a clear vision of the unique path in life

THE GALLBLADDER:
Blocked Anger

The gallbladder is called the "decision-maker." That is its function: to help you make decisions. It is said that the interaction between the gallbladder and liver energies—again, these are the spring/wood organs— empower your ability to see your inner and outer worlds in an integrated way. (So within, so without.)

It is your decision-maker, the gallbladder, that facilitates deeper, more benevolent, and life-enhancing choices from minute to minute. Proper decision-making makes or breaks you. Without it, your life can veer off in any number of unfortunate ways. You can lose your direction.

The life force energy of the gallbladder, as well as the liver, is anger. Appropriate anger is your friend. Without it, you are subject to ever-changing winds. Without your anger, you're buggered.

Anger Turned Inward

She was married to a bit of a bully. However, from Kate's perspective, she and her husband had a fundamentally good and happy relationship. If she refrained from insulting his manhood (as he saw it) by getting involved in their finances, they got on just fine.

Kate had come to me claiming to be depressed with no sense of horizon. She referred to her sense of hopelessness.

This was the first clue I was looking at an imbalance in a spring/wood organ.

Other common gallbladder symptoms include:

- Distension
- Skinny arms, skinny legs, but a tire around the midrange
- An angry demeanor and complaints of being faulted
- Chippy and jealous attitude
- "Hypochondriac" pain, primarily through the chest region
- On-and-off fever
- Thirst, with no desire to drink
- Bitter taste in the mouth
- Nausea, vomiting
- Inability to tolerate fats
- Seemingly no "oil" in your life, no easy flow

One day Kate's husband died. That's when she discovered that she genuinely had no idea what a mess he had been making of their lives, pensions, and financial arrangements. Not until the "appalling day" when her solicitor read the will and explained, in terrifying, minute detail, the mess with which she had been left. Kate was in trouble, to be precise.

She sighed a lot when she arrived at the clinic. Each sigh gave off a heavy sense of hopelessness. One of the most telling symptoms of a gallbladder imbalance is the tendency for the patient to sigh a lot. They will try their best to get a breath because when your emotions get stuck, they become manifest in the physical, primarily in breathing rhythms.

Kate had no idea what moves she should make. She often woke in the night, she complained, and then could not get back to sleep for hours. When she finally nodded off again, she would be restless. When I asked if she felt any anger toward her husband, she nervously replied, "No, no, not at all. Poor Bunny, he must have felt so alone having refused to let me help him. It's so sad as I am good at figures. What a mess, what a terrible mess, there is no hope, none at all." She came across as extraordinarily timid, indecisive, far more than usual.

Kate's anger, in other words, had become blocked. That block played out inside her body and in her relationships.

Stagnant spring energy can seemingly lie dormant until it turns to the inner winds and becomes frustration, then blocked anger, then rage. What begins as a breeze can grow into gale-force winds sooner or later, in some form. The dynamic expression of this spiraling energy within us needs to be given direction. It can lash outward in unexpected ways or, if unexpressed, anger can quickly turn in on itself. As was the case with Kate, you can become timid and unsure. The life-force energy becomes weakened, empty.

It was Kate's timidity that gave her stepson the idea that he could ride roughshod over her once the will was read and ignore his father's wishes. Having been left the estate as the sole beneficiary, Kate had total power over this stepson who was attempting to rob her of what could be salvaged. Still, her weakened energy would not allow her to respond properly.

I listened for some time until I finally said, "God, I'd be angry. You're not angry yet? Can I help you get angry? Even a tiny bit? No? Then there's something wrong with you."

In our society, anger gets a bad rap. When people talk about anger—rage, in particular—they do not understand it as natural energy. Most people are terrified of anger. They have no sense of how dynamic and collaborative it is.

Anger, when cleanly directed against someone trying to bully you, for instance, is incredibly useful and healthy. Instead of meeting aggression with more aggression, having a hissy fit, or further engaging it with a defensive line of questioning ("Why are you being so rude to me?"), anger energy can be very directive and amused. The attempt to intimidate you can be bashed off with an energetic flip of the wrist. Anger energy can take the form of straightforward assertiveness and send the message that you're not to be taken advantage of in any way.

As soon as you give someone permission to be angry—as soon as you tell them that it's appropriate—you can practically see them snap to.

Though it took time, Kate began to recognize the ways that she had suppressed her life force to be happy in her marriage. It was she, she came to see, not the accountants, lawyers, or any of the other parties involved to "help" her—it was she who would find the solution to her mess. Kate not only prevented bankruptcy but was able to turn the estate into something quite profitable. And so, she thrived.

Her timidity disappeared, her nerves were as steady as a rock, and she ended up gaining the reputation of a poker player—very steely but fair. No one dared try to take advantage of her again.

It amused her how much she had changed. "Of course, I love being who I am now, but Bunny was not secure enough to have liked these aspects of me at all. Our marriage would never have lasted. Perhaps, deep down, I knew how insecure he was, so I suppose I chose to keep being the timid, nervous one in our relationship so that he could appear to shine."

Sometimes people get stuck in an awful relationship because they need to learn to be a loving human being, not because they are an idiot. Being with an abusive person allows them to develop some muscles they would not otherwise develop. That relationship may be a fantastic gym that enables them to evolve.

And that is a philosophical difference between ICM and the Western health system. Sometimes the problem—complete with painful symptoms—is the solution to something far more extensive.

The Other Prong

In the UK, an electrical plug has three prongs, each connected to its own wire. You need all three—prongs and wires—to safely access and harness the force of electricity. When one of those wires is shorted, problems arise. Balance must be restored. The weakness must be redirected, thereby becoming a strength.

Spring/wood energy, like an electrical plug, can short out in many ways. Not only can an imbalance cause a person to become timid and weak, but it can also come across as bullying and arrogance—complete with a staccato voice—which defies anyone to question what appears to be their authority. Assertiveness, charisma, hostility, and benevolence are part of the mix of anger; they are prongs.

It is said that the greatest world leaders need to have their strength and weakness in the wood element. Firm backbone aside, you don't have to look very far to see how an imbalance can wreak havoc.

Of course, there are various signs of imbalance that fall between extremes.

A runner named David came to me as his tendons were bothering him. Tendons, by the way, are very much connected to the gallbladder. He was inflexible and rigid about running and would not cut back on his scheduled regimen. He flatly refused.

As I assessed him, we chatted. Beyond his annoyance with his misbehaving tendon, David was furious about the injustice in a political situation in another country… absolutely furious.

Deeper into the conversation, we came upon the subject of his son, who was being bullied. Instead of being outraged, David came across as apathetic. I didn't know why he had dropped the topic into the conversation, but then he suggested that the bullying might be good for his son as he, too, had been bullied. Where he spent his energy, his anger, I found curious.

Interested in the drop of tone in his voice when discussing this, I asked David about the bullying he'd been subjected to. He became almost shifty, wrapping his arms firmly around his body and looking away.

During treatment, he began to open up. Early on, David had been badly shamed, humiliated, and verbally bullied, even by his teachers. He was picked on because he was incredibly intelligent and ahead of everyone else. Instead of being praised or encouraged for being so clever, David had been isolated.

He hadn't realized how much he had hated his cleverness, the pain it had caused him. His suppressed rage was the driving force behind him seeking justice in places that were not his direct responsibility. This he did because he felt so powerless over situations far closer to home, namely that of his son. I explained to him that wood energy can give us a tremendous sense of compassion and benevolence toward the world but can easily be misdirected, too.

I gave him a couple of examples. For instance, a wealthy bene-factor will share his land with neglected zoo animals but will continually forget to feed his dog. Or a lawyer will walk in with a swagger, treating clients and the office staff as if they are idiots, and yet tend to his orchids with infinite care and attention. Green in the face—a flashing beacon to anyone qualified to see how distressed his gallbladder is—he is stretched and irritable in all areas of his life, except with his orchids, which don't answer back.

"I must do something about my son," he said one day. His voice became strong and assertive, crystal clear. "Like me, he's very clever and I'm simply ignoring the problem. Of course, I can do something about it now. I am an adult."

David committed to spending more time and energy on his family. He could see that he had been misdirecting his resources.

While I worked on his tendons, he laughed. "I've been activating my tendons in the wrong way, haven't I?" He could see the connections. "I'm even feeling less rigid about my training. Has that been damaging me? Was I running from all of that bottled-up and unresolved stuff from my past?"

By learning to befriend his buried frustration, David discovered himself.

When You Know Better, You Do Better

Again, your problem often contains not only your weakness but your strengths as well. In other words, within your weakness is your greatest level of potential, your area for deepest insight. With such insight comes an ability to make different decisions. Balanced gallbladder energy can lead to decisions that create a way forward despite every block. All resistance can be incorporated into these decisions.

Inwardly, you can make decisions even if it is impossible to act on them. None of us will escape those moments in life when it seems as though we have no choice, at least outwardly. We all come up against the kind of resistance that makes us want to surrender. Even then, your choices will take you one way or another. Even then, you can have peace because you know where you want to wind up.

THE LIVER:
Indignation

In ICM, the liver is thought of as the general who carries out the plans for your life. Strategy is born of healthy liver energy, as are sound decisions. The liver governs your behavior. It mediates your emotions—anger, a sense of lacking, frustration, irritability, and depression—and provides the ability to define yourself in the world in relation to your work, family, and friends, so you can develop over time and ensure your future direction. Healthy liver energy is evidenced in excitement, in hope for the future. In the sense that someone's at the helm—the general—saying, "You can do it. You can do it."

The keywords for the liver energy are growth, birth, assertion, vision, basic needs provided, structure, organization, and boundaries. The liver is about the potential for life on every level. Can that relationship develop? Can I experience more love and vibrational joy? Can I become richer, better, more glorious, and wiser?

Your liver cracks your emotional state. The free flow of its energy allows for greater vision, complete with benevolence, not blatant anger and arrogance. Within your spring/wood energy, your liver strongly affects your emotional life alongside the dual aspects of your spirituality, which is deeply rooted in your sexuality.

Anger, the ancient Chinese believed, gives birth to sexuality. As you develop as a human being, your spirituality, essence, and sexuality spring from the pelvis area. The spring/wood energy activates all in quite an organic way.

Physical, emotional, and sexual manifestations abound when this energy is out of balance. Signs of an imbalance include:

- Chronic belching with regurgitation
- Aimlessness and malaise
- Depression
- A loss of interest in sex
- Tendon issues
- Weak or brittle nails
- Emotional lability

The Straying Father-in-Law

He described the tension in his body, the plum-sensation he had stuck in his throat. It was taking everything he had to refrain from snapping at his children. On the way to the clinic, "some idiot" had cut across him in traffic and nearly crashed into him. Richard's instant rage had frightened him more than "the idiot" had. He had no idea what was going on with him. "I'm not myself at all. I'm like a pressure cooker just about to go off."

As I examined him, Richard discussed the primary reason he had landed in my clinic. He had pulled a muscle while exercising to burn off his frustration and tension. He needed me to help him release the pressure.

But there was more.

Often people come to me because they have heard that I am great at sorting out life during times of change. Such was the case with Richard. These patients may not know quite what is wrong with them; they just sense that I can help. Part of what draws people to me is my wood energy, as flexible as it is. My six-week waiting list in two different places is born of people responding to that energy, the assertiveness and confidence of well-directed wood energy. There is no hostility or timidity, which is part of the energetic spectrum, but there is kindness.

I asked Richard, "Is there anything that has recently happened that has made you furious and also confused?"

He explained that he had discovered that his father-in-law was having an affair. The man knew that Richard was on to the affair and had asked him to keep mum. This infuriated Richard. The father-in-law demonstrated zero respect or remorse, only an apparent obsessive need to carry on with the deceit.

"It's what my dad did to my mom," Richard said. "I'm livid but I can't yet talk to my wife without knowing what my plan is. It's a relief to tell you about it; in fact, I already feel less tense." Then he thought again. He paused, unsure if he should go further. "My mojo has gone out from underneath me. I have no energy, and I'm lethargic when I'm not furious."

He explained how he was no longer having sex with his wife, though they loved each other. When I nodded my head in acknowledgment, he added one more complaint. "I've also noticed my sense of trust and faith in something bigger than myself has been affected, which has me shaken."

I recognized that his father-in-law's behavior triggered Richard's childhood trauma.

Richard's issues were not just a problem to be solved but an opportunity. The dilemma he was facing was a chance for him to grow.

As you mature, which is what you are meant to do, the spring/wood energy grows through you, the way it might in a tree trunk, so that sex is no longer just an act but a way to make love. The goal becomes a greater sense of connectedness, instead of an impersonal release.

Richard's energy imbalance had left him feeling not only angry but disconnected from his wife and his mojo. He had been cast adrift. We would work together to transform his fury, smooth out the emotional frustration and rage. While I worked on balancing his liver energy, we spoke about how he might handle the situation.

Eventually, Richard's balanced liver energy allowed him to better plan and discern how to handle a potentially impossible situation. He was then able to confront the problem. He set clear boundaries and spelled out the consequences of his father-in-law's continued bad behavior.

This was when he learned that his father-in-law had recently been diagnosed as diabetic and had taken it very hard. He was depressed and afraid that his youth was slipping away. His behavior was the result.

With the benevolence and softness that can come from clear liver energy, Richard could see what was behind his father-in-law's actions. When you can see what is really happening, you can bend and be flexible on all levels. You can see beyond your hurt and anger.

Transforming Richard's rage also required that he separate the present dilemma from the past hurt his father's behavior had caused, which was caught in his cells.

His internal vision needed to be shifted away from his childhood experience to now giving his father-in-law a chance.

In his willingness to work with the layers of what was happening, Richard was able to affect not just himself but also the others involved. When he addressed the imbalance within, those around him grew healthier.

"I seem much more rooted in the bigger picture, which is what ultimately my father-in-law has responded to. He was able to understand that he was operating momentarily from his hurt, confusion, and sense of what he perceived was his impending decline."

When he found more compassion for his father-in-law, Richard's mojo returned, and his happy sex life revived.

Healthy wood energy will be kind and not too self-righteous. Through the power of liver energy, you can be moderate around the need to rest and also be active in your days. You can express the energy around your frustrations and your emotional state in healthy ways, allowing for each turn of your spring energy to propel you into more personal growth. This growth will allow for the internal integration between your sexuality and your spirituality.

The Crime of Jumping the Queue

You can quickly become self-righteous. When faced with the opportunity (or choice) to be compassionate or flexible, you can fall at the first hurdle daily. I certainly do, repeatedly. But I am also able to acknowledge where my own choice is changing me, and that helps me to become more integrated from the inside out. That is your liver energy at work.

Even the most "spiritual" among us have plenty of room for growth in this department.

The other day, a friend jumped into a very long queue with me. I often have to use my walking stick, particularly when having a nasty time with pain. Looking at a long, winding staircase up and then down to where, eventually, we would be seated, my friend kindly took charge and politely asked if we could be accepted into the queue halfway down, thereby saving me great distress.

However, what was amusing was that most of the people in the queue, who were waiting to hear one of the leading spiritual teachers of the day, became angry. Oh, the fuss that spun out at us as we were belligerently accepted into the queue. People all around us held onto resentments and their rigid series of judgments, so much so that I suspect none of them even saw my walking stick. They were far more comfortable sitting in their indignant fury at the very idea of two people jumping the queue. They could not discern what was going on. Indignation had left them blind.

A Sustainable Equilibrium

The nature of anger within your liver, your associated spring/wood energy, is expressed as a dynamic assertion accompanied by great clarity. Anger will assert itself as a shoot, which is even capable of somehow finding its way through concrete. Misplaced anger can leave you railing against something not your business, baying at the moon.

You know your liver is in balance when you can respond to life and its endless frustrations by sustaining equilibrium with flexibility that keeps you in a state of inner harmony, focused on your internal strategy. You can remain structured in your days, but not overly so, capable of putting boundaries up as you go.

IV.
Summer/Fire

The Season of
CARTWHEELING FOR JOY

Your summer season brings out that warmth and ability to not take too much too seriously. Fire, the element associated with summer, is about bubbly, playful expansiveness. Those with a strong summer/fire energy tend to be the life of the party: spontaneous, big on variety, fun.

I cannot deny that my mother had a lot of fire in her. She made the lives of many others slightly easier with her immense humor, dare, and outrageous style.

I once asked why she was cartwheeling down Beauchamp Place, a stylish street in the heart of London. Of course, being very young, I didn't know whether to be appalled and embarrassed or really rather proud of my hippy mother.

"For fun, darling. Why?"

That is the summer/fire energy at play.

When your summer/fire systems are in balance, laughter and joy spill out easily. Internally, you can take yourself very lightly when the fire is steady. It is your summer/fire energy that responds with fun, laughter, and merriment to life and is deeply connected to your interactions with others. Relationships can improve immensely with just the art of laughing at yourself.

Have you ever noticed that when talking about subjects you love, you get "fired up"? Watch the reactions of others when watching a play, ballet, film, or sport—their whole faces are animated; watch when an attractive person walks into a room or when someone pays another attention. Sexual chemistry is presumed to be and is marketed as being solely based on relatively superficial criteria. However, when a person is animated and in their authority, they can be very magnetic to all of life. When the internal fire is strong, the magnetic force between people is usually easy to feel, see, and hear; on all levels, it is obvious.

Of course, you can also become deficient in summer/fire energy. This can look like sleep issues, intimacy/relationship issues, feeling flat, a lack of joy. When you're deficient, you may have trouble connecting, experiencing joy, or being spontaneous; you can feel like there's something wrong with you.

Your fire, internally and externally, allows you the ability to give and receive love with appropriate degrees of emotional closeness. It helps you know how and when to be open or shut to people. Some people literally know how to turn the switch to their magnetic force field on or off, which is always fascinating to watch. Part of evolving and maturing is discovering that you, too, have a switch inside of you that you can consciously operate with integrity.

Imagine the ignition switch that lights the fire or the gas in a home; that is what you can learn to do for yourself with increasing effectiveness.

And when there is an imbalance in your summer/fire energy, your ability to let people in or keep them out is jeopardized.

Your fires will do whatever it takes to keep your embers going, however inappropriate it seems on the outside. When you are desperate for warmth, you will grab on to it from pure survival and adrenalize your fear; you will do whatever it takes to make a fire.

It takes time to learn how to fuel the embers from sustainable interactions that keep you warm, evenly, and on all levels.

When you have old and unresolved issues of the summer/fire energy and genuine love comes into your life, there will come a point when you can, unintentionally, project old hurts or wounds onto the new object of your love. Trust versus betrayal is a paramount issue for the two gates within your system.

The summer season within us, the official of balance and harmony, has four different energy systems which harmonize your fire energy. These systems always ensure that your throne—your heart—is kept safe and guarded while maintaining temperatures that stay steady throughout the many changes around it. When in balance and working steadily on your behalf, intimacy is spontaneous and without conscious thought.

Summer organs include:

- Triple burner
- Small intestine
- Pericardium
- Heart

Other summer associations that inform diagnosis:

- Element—fire
- Emotion/energy—joy and radiance

A *balanced* summer provides the ability to:

- Give and receive love with appropriate degrees of emotional closeness

- Know how and when it is okay to open or shut down to others
- Decide how much to open to others in all different forms of relationships

THE TRIPLE BURNER:
Blowing Hot and Cold

When I was a child, I remember hearing a mechanic describe what was wrong with my father's car: "She's gone on the blink, sir, good and proper like."

"Going on the blink" is a brilliant expression for what happens when the thermostat in your life is asking for more balance and harmony.

The triple burner, which is essentially your thermostat, is your first line of defense in your body's fire system. (The triple burner is the ICM term, but we'll go with "thermostat," because you can better relate to the term.) When working correctly, your thermostat can bring a sense of warmth, spontaneous joy, and laughter to all sorts of situations. It can bring about a sudden and needed burst of heat, fluid release, or sweat. When your thermostat is in balance, it partially maintains the homeostasis for your receiving, processing, and eliminating.

When your thermostat is on the blink or not working at its maximum, you can have a multitude of dilemmas and challenges going on all at once; your body will struggle to keep your temperature even on multiple levels, physically, emotionally, and spiritually.

Just as issues arise from setting the heating in your house too high (or conversely, letting your home grow cold), they occur in your system. You need to know how and when to turn up the thermostat to maintain balance and support the heart, preferably in an automatic way rather than forcibly overriding the system.

An Energetic Re-Direct

When your thermostat gets caught up in a greater priority which involves your overall health and well-being or, from a Western perspective, your immune system is being compromised, the energy gets diverted.

In the United States, where I have had a lot of procedures done, nurses have placed warmed blankets on me as I came around, ice-cold and in extreme shock. I would feel incredibly shaky, tearful, and anxious, yet those blankets served as the first line of defense for my regulation, which was offline.

Back home in England, I would find that I needed vast support in my everyday functioning. I felt punch drunk with my temperature controls on the blink, even though my energy was directed toward putting out other fires and working hard on the healing process.

Emotionally, my responses to nearly everything seemed slow, flat, and lifeless as I struggled to regain something that I remembered but could no longer self-generate. I was a fully-fledged waxwork of my former self, ghost-like. I needed to have someone either in the room or lying with me holding my hand. No amount of hot water bottles or blankets would reheat me. All the energy had gone to the source of the immediate priority. Like a sprinkler system defending a home from fire, nothing but the emergency mattered

The following are just some of the physical symptoms that can arise from the triple burner energy being on the blink:

- Heart palpitations
- Agitation
- Insomnia
- Dream-disturbed sleep
- Being easily startled
- Spontaneous sweating
- Feelings of cold or heat

Now, an energetic re-direct can create a whole host of problems, not just physical, but emotional, relational, or spiritual.

With a thermostat on the blink, you may find it tricky to sustain loving and connected relationships. You might blow hot and cold with your dear ones, giving off conflicting messages, withdrawing, and shutting down while seemingly inviting interactions at the same time.

If you have never experienced it yourself, you may have noticed an obvious spark igniting between two people upon meeting. Initially, the connection appears very flirty and fun, wonderful to observe. However, before your very eyes, what appeared to be full of possibility turns into a mess of conflicting emotions. One or both start blowing hot and cold as if neither of them has enough internal fire to sustain the flame.

Blowing hot and cold: that's an excellent metaphor for this aspect of your struggling feedback system.

Your thermostat energy will decide if it is appropriate to allow someone in further or closer to your heart, to assess potential damage that could invade your inner sanctuary where the heart is governing your whole body. But when it's compromised, it can fail to do its job.

Early Trauma

Often, when a person has too much shock or trauma in their younger life, it is as if the thermostat has gone on the blink. Take the case of my patient, Samuel.

"She is not available. I've played this game for long enough that I want to figure out my part in it. Sometimes I think I'm only attracted to unavailable women. If they were actually open to a decent, long-term relationship, I honestly think I would run a mile.

"Real intimacy terrifies me. I can be all over someone like a rash one moment and then suddenly cold if they respond.

"I keep so many friendships going on all at once in a sort of frothy, bubbling way but make damn sure no one gets too close. I never have one-on-ones with anyone.

"I run hot and cold all of the time."

These remarks made me curious about the state of Samuel's triple burner, the thermostat within the summer/fire energy. They all indicated that his thermostat was not working at a steady and even temperature.

He longed for intimacy, closeness, and validation on the outside when, in fact, he sent out all the wrong signals.

Due to my reputation, he'd become curious, so to my clinic he'd come.

Samuel's behavior, choices, and decisions around connections and relationships had become too guarded, or inappropriately open. On the one hand, he was allowing untrustworthy people beyond his inner guards, making it difficult to expel them from his realm, leaving him far too open and exposed to adequately protect himself. On the other hand, he held safe and reliably warm and loving people at bay. In with the bad, out with the good.

It had come time for Samuel to honestly face all the challenging, early experiences he had—because the nexus of the problem lay in the past. He had been burnt up inside at a very early age and left with the inability to protect himself. It was as if the guards at the gates of his inner sanctuary had been overwhelmed, rendered incapable of doing the job they were meant to do. His heart had closed off with the sheer velocity of blows he had received from people, events, and consequences. The embers had very nearly gone out. Equally, those embers would suddenly and erratically burst into flame and give others a false sense of unsustainable warmth.

It was imperative for Samuel's well-being that he begin to undertake a serious review of his energy state so he could learn to manage, if not automate, his thermostat. It would have been all too easy to get stuck in a vicious cycle of focusing on what had been done to him in childhood rather than dealing with the stark consequences of his ongoing responses to a deeply confusing childhood. (The details of which, for practical purposes, are irrelevant.)

One of the first homework assignments I gave Samuel was to find people he admired, people who seemed to have trustworthy, intimate relationships. He was to observe from a distance, at least initially, what it looked and felt like, so as not to become frightened by the proximity.

I also wanted him to see if he could find examples of the rhythms of nature all around him. I recommended watching nature programs, with a particular focus on the courting rituals of animals, such as the dancing that goes on in the mating seasons. I asked him to avoid the animals that end up eating their mate once they have made love, to which he chuckled.

With time, Samuel's emotional volatility, confusion, and sense of not being loveable were transformed into mainly feeling loveable, content, and at home emotionally. His choices became warmer and more consistent with all types of interactions. He did not make so many absolute relationship pickles once his thermostat came on duty again.

As he recovered, through grieving the losses involved in not having a safe childhood, he began to understand that he would always be vulnerable in his thermostat area. Still, equally, it could be his greatest asset and strength. Samuel had been taught to deeply mistrust his body, so he was doing what so many of us do: mistrusting his feedback mechanism.

He also began to see how he would use people, places, and events as a kind of mood-altering activity, which works, albeit poorly, but needed to be understood before his systems failed.

Constant activity and dependence on distraction often keep your actual needs hidden. Whitewashing challenges with quick and ultimately futile fixes only prolongs the discomfort and unresolved pain that, in the case of the fire energy, either produces a faltering thermostat or a raging, overheating one that carries scalding water in its piping.

To master his fire energy and functions, Samuel had to commit to learning all he could about what works in liberating us internally, connecting us to abundant life. He had to transition from an intellectual understanding of what needed to happen to the embodiment of it.

A lack of profound knowing would never produce the long-term and sustainable energy/heat he was after—one that would support vibrant health. To make sustainable fires, he would need to choose very differently who he could and could not be intimate with, and who would be safe for him to take time to get to know.

With his earlier experiences faced and having acknowledged that his original survival tactics had kept him alive, he discovered that they were no longer working; in fact, they were backfiring horribly on him. He would need courage to allow himself to be joyful from a much deeper place.

Accepting that quick fixes cannot work (bar emergencies when you need rapid solutions) one must be willing to embrace a deeper foundation of self-awareness in mind, body, and spirit.

For Samuel, it was vital to grasp that the quick fixes ultimately robbed him of understanding the brilliance of his functioning—that he was able to keep himself free of the tangled webs of childhood. He needed to rekindle the embers that were still steady and burning within him. He also needed to learn how to grieve, not just on an intellectual level. In the still of night, there was much that he needed to gently allow himself to come to terms with: the very things that had affected his fire so deeply. His relationship with himself needed stoking.

No journey is ever "job done;" it is season by season. Your internal thermostat needs to be looked after and serviced alongside your heating and water systems regularly—you cannot afford to take them for granted.

The Lure of Frothy Entanglements

I have had deep friendships with amazing women whose strengths and potential area for growth/strengthening/stretching were in their thermostats. In hindsight, I wish I had known what I know now about the fragilities/strengths of this energetic pattern. I would have saved myself some heartache.

When they interacted with the world, these women were all very engaging, available, and attentive. They were very shiny, as if the fire in the room came from them. I never fully realized, though, that just because they sustained that level of warmth outwardly did not necessarily mean they had it inside themselves. They were in survival mode; they kept others at bay, rather than exposing how deficient they felt. It was almost as if they felt compelled to convey a false fire, to keep themselves internally stable. But each one could withdraw, shut down, or suddenly become bitchy without warning. The fire within them would suddenly die.

You can probably imagine how important this aspect of the summer season and your fire is on an emotional, spiritual level in connection to yourself and others.

On days when you are just below your lines of stability or just plain miserable, your thermostat requires you to become better at being kind—at giving yourself the same warmth, attention, and gentle encouragement that you would to a friend.

On those days when everyone around you seems enraged, snarky, tearful, or all over the place, it's easy to run into frothy entanglements—things that create drama to distract you from that to which your clever system is trying to alert you.

Yet, if you can remain calm, the storm around you will tend to settle. Chaos need not escalate for you or others. As the extremes in your heating and water systems become balanced, you place less emphasis on extremes within and outside of yourself.

A sense of lightness and humor will ripple through your internal kingdom when you truly understand that you have control of your switches, when you are the master of your thermostat dial. Such vitality, sense of well-being, and inner equilibrium can be had no matter the circumstances once you can take regular and consistent responsibility for your actions and behaviors, never blaming another.

Managing Your Feedback System

Oh, the brilliance of the feedback mechanism; it continually runs, all the time. The key is to get to know it. Life affords you that opportunity.

Life is not often marketed as a series of events that allow you to get the hang of your navigational system—but that's what it is.

The first step is to willingly be with your dis-ease, to meet yourself where you are, to feel safe, and be honest about everything—including the mess you may make of your relationships.

After all, to be good at anything in life, including relationships and self-management, you must first start understanding your equipment and feedback systems. That's the role your thermostat (your triple burner) plays.

THE SMALL INTESTINE:
Muddled

The function of the small intestine is to *separate the pure from the impure*. It controls the reception, transformation, and separation of solids and fluids.

Physical manifestations of an unhappy small intestine include:

- Abdominal pain
- Scanty dark urine
- Burning pain on urination
- Severe restlessness
- Mouth ulcers
- A twisting pain that goes around to your back
- A stiff neck that cannot be turned from side to side (energy lines for your small intestine go through your neck)

Like other organs, the small intestine plays a mental role as well. Remember, you are an amalgam of body, mind, and spirit—all of which must be examined in terms of energy imbalance.

This form of communication by an organ usually overlooked by Western medicine is invaluable. The mental role of the small intestine is to separate the clear thoughts from the turbid ones. Clear judgment depends on the ability to separate these two types of thoughts. Clear judgment results in clear and consistent behavior.

When not working correctly, the small intestine can cause your behaviors to seem two-faced, muddling the purity, of, say, your friendships. It plays out in many ways. For example, you may participate in momentary power struggles with juicy gossip behind your friend's back, rather than remain supportive or kind. You may be cruel to your partner and yet seemingly gracious to others. You may give your best aspects to the outside world while sharing only your most toxic traits with those you claim to love.

Unfortunately, you may participate in any number of toxic behaviors without having a clue: bullying, shaming, blaming, scapegoating, humiliation, projection, jealousy, arrogance, snubbing, manipulation, scheming, and so on. When this becomes your modus operandi, you have a marked imbalance.

Waking up to some of your unpleasant behaviors, traits, and patterns can be difficult—but also enormously liberating and healing. Sometimes the stories and reasons behind your actions become irrelevant as you switch your intention and focus, as you catch your toxic reactions and learn to respond appropriately.

Generally, to change how you relate to others, you must start with how you relate to yourself.

Once you learn to stop judging, bullying, and shaming yourself—that internal dialogue that continually runs through your mind, creating turbidity—you can neutrally assess what you are up to that needs sorting and changing.

You can be the problem in your own life—but happily, you can also be the immediate solution.

No matter what is happening and whatever circumstances you find yourself in, you can only ever master yourself. When you can begin to take responsibility for your side of anything, your living and your relationships subsequently become clearer and cleaner.

The Ultimate Mixed Message

When you operate inconsistently because of muddled thinking (a symptom of an imbalanced small intestine and its associated summer/fire energy), you can queer your relationships. Take, for example, the attractive man who walked into my treatment room and launched into his story.

"A wild cat has just walked into the middle of my world, stunning as hell, and turned my world inside out and upside down. You see, I'm gay, and I've never fancied a woman. This one, though— jeepers!"

Phillip explained that the woman knew he was gay, or at least had assumed as much, and not bisexual. "She knows but won't accept that it's now only her that I want, which I respect as all my gay friends tell me I'm off my rocker and cannot possibly, suddenly, be so turned on by a woman."

None of the characters in Phillip's life got the sudden change, least of all the object of his inexplicable ardor. "In my bones and my soul, I know she's my soul mate. There won't be anyone else like her for me. It goes totally beyond gender."

In clinical practice and beyond, I have witnessed many shifts in the expression of people's sexuality, as it is never an isolated expression. I acknowledged as much.

"How on earth can I accept either that she will never trust me, therefore not become my wife, let alone be in a relationship with me; or that by taking this path, which I completely want, I must also lose all my friends?"

Phillip's friends were ganging up on him, presumably, threatened by this utter shift in him. Something had happened that was beyond his control, and he was looking for help. He had been exposed to the philosophy and ancient wisdom of the East, which is what led him to my door. "It's time for me to sack my present committee and serve all the directors notice."

My ears perked because this was a novel and insightful way of referring to your internal and external dialogue, the voices in your head that must always be sorted. I asked him about this phrasing.

"You see, when I was very young, my father helped me come to terms with my sexuality. He introduced me to the idea that I have a group of directors in my mind, alongside a committee of either gaggling geese, as he used to call them, or serene swans, that are on my side in all matters." His father had gone on to teach him that, periodically, you need to be willing to be ruthless, if necessary, and sack any committee members or directors that are unsupportive.

We all have voices in our heads—usually taken from parents or other remnants of the past—which do not necessarily serve us. Thinking of those voices as committee members in your mind's boardroom is a great way to address them and get them off your back, so you can move forward and flourish in life.

You have the power to sack them all if they are not serving you—just as that patient's father taught him. You can replace them with committee members that are on your side; that way, when the inevitable "shit hits the fan," you take charge of your board-room. When you become aware of what your differing voices are saying—that internal dialogue—you can find ways of quieting your mind at will.

You can also master how you are being treated outwardly. For as sure as an egg is an egg, if you are allowing an internal bully to have a voice, then you will also have an external one.

To make a long-ish story short, Phillip went on to live "happily ever after" with the bride of his soul's choice, but not before going through some incredibly brave transitions that were humbling to witness.

Phillip dug deep into his behavior. He recognized that, from way back when, he was usually "murky" in his relationships; he often opted for the "murkier and nastier" ways of expressing his sexuality, which were far removed from love and cornerstones of safe and lasting relationships. He also realized that he had never consciously practiced intimacy and all that it entails.

He no longer wanted to continue behaving in the same split ways. He wanted to live in integrity.

The real reason Phillip's friends walked away from him had nothing to do with the shift in the expression of his sexuality; it was because he had never really let them see the real him, the one he was most comfortable with, the one he trusted more.

"It was just another betrayal on my part—my being so false with them." His sudden expression of wholehearted passion and connection with another human being had been what shook them. It made them realize how shallow he had been with them.

"Her appearance in my life had made the two aspects of my behavior collide, making it impossible for me not to begin to be congruent."

This lack of congruency, his desire for real and lasting change to take place, had caused Phillip to call out to this woman unconsciously. That's how clever his body was in its attempt to balance his fire energy.

Phillip took a year to initially come to terms with such a vast shift in his whole orientation while becoming a trusted friend to this woman. Only in the second year of knowing him did she begin to allow herself to fall in love and be willing to contemplate being with him.

All That You Magnetize

If you are a person, like me, who wants nothing more than to be an example of what is possible, you may want to pay close attention to this next bit.

When imbalanced, you can magnetize people, situations, or events that reflect your dysfunction. The more resistance you have internally in your organs, the more you automatically become a magnet for malfunction outside of yourself, and have little capacity to deal with it all.

It is the small intestine's job to sort out whether you need to prepare yourself to help when a fellow human is in trouble—but sometimes you must prepare yourself for the shifting sands that may suck you in when others cannot or will not sort through their stuff.

You may be drawing these people to you without the resources to give them (or you) what they (you) need, which can distract you from your health and growth. This is why the health of your small intestine is of paramount importance.

My mother had an expression that continually proves to be accurate, though not quite as she meant it: "No good deed ever goes unpunished." I always associate this maxim with the small intestine energy, as it is the mastering of your own internal committee that allows you to have the wisdom and maturity to assess what will happen when you feel led to do a "good deed."

My father (thank God for the unique balance of both of my parents' wisdom) taught us that when we are in a position to support, help, or encourage others, as we'd been encouraged to do from an early age, the very person who had turned to you in their vulnerability will often walk away without so much as a thank you. He explained that most people want no reminders of what it was like to be so out of control, vulnerable, or reliant on another person, so they subconsciously rid themselves of you. Hence, no good deed goes unpunished.

Of course, this is not always true.

Yet, to stick to the intention of being a profoundly good practitioner, just like those who have impacted my life dramatically for the better, I have had to be continually willing to keep being open to my inner awakening. I know that to assist others, I must be healthy. Part of the strength required to do so comes from also accepting my frailties. I suggest the same holds for you.

Feed Yourself First

By responding to others through the lens of your misconceptions about yourself, you can enable more problems than solutions. Hence, it becomes paramount that the focus must be on taking responsibility for your inner health first to be of real value to others in your world.

THE HEART:
Overly Agreeable

In ICM, the heart is known as the Supreme Controller, the office of Lord and Sovereign. This makes sense because your heart will serve you to its last heartbeat, literally, with nary a moment off as it continues to pump blood and oxygen to every corner of your energetic systems. Fairly, justly, and neutrally, it pumps and beats in rhythm twenty-four hours a day, seven days a week.

When your heart is in trouble on a physical level, you may experience:

- High or low blood pressure
- High cholesterol
- Inflammatory states
- Nutritional deficiencies
- The tendency to drink or party excessively
- Leg and lower back pain
- Arteriolosclerosis

Alongside its three counterparts—the small intestine, the triple burner-thermostat, and the pericardium—the heart continually aligns with your integrated truths. Emotionally, when the heart is in balance, the love that automatically flows from it is visceral, not just intellectual. It will show you that what you want is what you need to become your true self. The heart dictates the love that you so often want from others. This love is the very foundation of joy.

Spiritually, your heart holds what is called the *shen*, which is the heart's energy. Without knowing it, you may wander around with a *shen* disturbance. It's as if you are no longer at home. The sparkle in your eyes has dimmed.

You can be funny, the "life of the party," and still be spiritually flat inside because you lack the radiance your heart needs to truly mature or know joy. When your heart is not energetically aligned with your true desires and needs, you can be compulsively cheerful, giving the impression of being in a state of joy when, in fact, the opposite is true. That, in turn, means that the wrong signals are given out in your life force, so your needs are never met.

A spiritual imbalance is often far more pronounced than any single physical ailment of the heart.

Spiritual Spinning

I learned to be an effective spiritual spinner, topping and tailing my emotional states. I needed to fit in and attain approval, so I plastered over my true emotional response to whatever was happening in my life.

From an early age, I sensed that my real internal responses to external stimuli were considered wrong. I believed that there were negative and positive emotions (when an infinite variety of opposing states and frequencies coexist). Therefore, no emotional state is either good or bad, positive or negative, yet I didn't know that until far too late.

My spiritual spinning was so effective for so long that it allowed me to bypass all sorts of grieving, frustrations, and appropriate emotional responses to the medical challenges and dramas to which I always, sooner or later, returned. My spiritual spinning went into overdrive every time painful emotions came up around the powerlessness of my medical condition, emotions which I judged as wrong, something to be bypassed as quickly as possible. I became adept at avoiding and diverting my attention—and that of others—away from my accumulating losses.

As I busied myself learning all sorts of tools to "deal" with my emotions, the words "resolving" or "recovering" never came up. Only later did I realize that feelings do not need to be dealt with— they need to be felt to their often-unfathomable depths, to become (quite possibly) the total opposite of whatever is experienced. That is how you balance your heart energy.

Again, I had never been allowed to have any of the appropriate emotional responses to my reality, let alone the shocks involved. Just as others denied the huge efforts it took me to achieve the basics that many people take for granted, I, too, denied my own needs. I looked well and able-bodied, but I was ill in ways that I now realize would have tipped many, if not most, people into a permanently switched-off state.

Unbeknownst to me, I had swallowed whole the reflections I had repeatedly experienced from Western and alternative medical practitioners—even from my profession. The collective reflection was one of almost no compassion, kindness, consideration, or encouragement to do what would have been appropriate.

No one had ever asked me how I was doing or feeling until the day arrived when some human sat in front of me, pre-surgery #575, and asked me, with a tear rolling down her cheek, how I had managed to stay intact. At that moment, the iceberg within me started to melt.

By spiritually spinning, topping, and tailing, I'd persuaded myself and others for years that I only felt extreme gratitude for the privilege of still being alive and able to walk. I was grateful for the incredible surgeon and team that had already done an extraordinary job with me.

Yet, I had no idea that all my spiritual spinning of huge gratitude was not serving me. Giving my life what I call "top spins" the whole time, as if I was playing tennis, had contributed to the creation of that iceberg, which would no longer be ignored. I found myself hitting a wall of grief and heartbreak that suddenly began to crumble inside me.

I had this story running in my head for so long that it hadn't occurred to me to consider what else my life's journey had meant—the cost to me, my body, my bank account, my career, my friendships, my love, and my family life.

The world loves what is now so tragically popular: "a positive person," "a positive spin." That façade is demoralizing and exhausting. No wonder, at last, my over-strained iceberg of grief was melting and crumbling.

I realized I was truly heartbroken, shattered by so much shock, on so many levels. My heart needed to mend and would do so by choosing to witness unconditionally, deeply, and intimately what I had gone through.

The body will eventually confront you with the truth, the whole truth, and nothing but the truth, "so help me, God."

Authentic, vibrant, energetic health furnishes you with an almost automatic response to life. So, when you are not engaging the wisdom of your feedback mechanisms, you respond to your pains, emotional and physical, by "topping" the surface of the pain. When this happens, you avoid the life-affirming experience of feeling all the emotions involved and are convinced that you have "dealt with" or "controlled" the response—you have "tailed" it.

This is not uncommon. Many of us do some form of topping and tailing of honest emotional responses to what's happening in life. But by refusing to acknowledge your genuine responses, by not knowing how to change gears energetically/emotionally, you unknowingly disable part of the vital satnav system within you.

Topping and tailing, rather than helping develop more self-knowledge, keeps your organs from developing energetically. By topping and tailing your emotions, you block your energy, your sense of aliveness and place yourself on the defensive. This often limits your awareness of your perspective, which again cuts you off from the very things you crave to be and to receive. By not being comfortable with all your emotions and keeping them in a balanced state, you find yourself instead overreacting to all sorts of outside stimuli, thus living in a very reactive state. You react to what is going on internally within you and accumulate clogged-up states; this taints your ability to respond to what is really in front of you. Ultimately, it costs you and others much more than you intended.

Layers of Hurt

Thomas lived with arteriosclerosis for many years. He had suffered three heart attacks and had six stents in place. At the root of his heart condition, however, was a combination of factors that, over time, had linked together to create the perfect storm for his physical body. These same factors contributed to further imbalances in his heart energy on other levels.

Thomas was in the business of providing high-profile hospitality. He was skilled at bringing others together, leading from the front, and keeping a demanding, sophisticated clientele extremely happy and entertained. He was entrusted to welcome and appropriately look after very high-ranking members of society, from politicians to royalty.

On the outside, Thomas's life was full of activity and stimulation from his work life, which appeared to be very joy-fueled and full of laughter. Yet, on the inside, his summer season was scorched flat. He struggled with heartbreak. He did not understand why he could not attain the types of relationships he longed for. He had always known that his interactions with people were off somehow, different than they were for others. He identified many relationships where he had been unable to be what others expected. He craved more interactions with others, yet he also had mechanisms within him that would appear to push them away, to signal that he did not want to be involved.

He lived with a constant sense of bewilderment and massive levels of frustration, never quite fulfilling the deepest yearnings of his own precious heart. His true hopes, dreams, and expectations of life seemed ever elusive. He contended with extreme levels of anxiety that always snapped at his *shen*.

Thomas was not able to put a voice to what had been happening. He kept our sessions light, controlled, and well-orchestrated on a sincere but entirely superficial level. He was charismatic, charming, and seemingly very sparkly. However, a very different story emerged when I read what we practitioners are trained to see, hear, touch, and experience.

Thomas was close to having a massive heart attack, one that would no doubt be his last. He suffered from terrible leg and lower back pains, which signaled more arterial blockages. He was deeply troubled and unhappy in his marriage but unaware of his own needs. An overlay of continuous, internally reactive rage—a real killing machine—kept him in a mist of misery.

It was a priority to bring change to bear as soon as possible, but not before I had fully grasped what was at play.

Very telling of the heart's energy, it came out that Thomas had experienced an extremely traumatic event during childhood. As a small boy learning to box, he won a championship against another boy. The very next day in assembly, it was announced to the whole school that the other boy had died.

As a direct result, and on a deep energetic level beyond words, Thomas had repressed any external guarding or protecting of his own domain from then on. The power of his punch had, to him, brought about another's death. The overlay of constantly not trusting his "punch," his security system, was in part playing a dangerous role in the perilous precipice upon which he stood. This was his heart's way of topping and tailing to keep him safe.

It was not that Thomas did not want to be involved with others, to form intimate relationships. Rather, his inner functioning was so fragile that he constantly had to protect himself as a priority, which left very little space to concentrate on anything outside of himself.

The layers of hurt within Thomas made perfect sense.

The adrenalized state that needed to counteract his ever-present anxiety, bordering on terror, was so extreme that it was impossible for his heart to be intimate or present in ways that others would expect or want. To be sincerely superficial and, in his case, magically so, was so alluring to his workplace, no one saw past it to understand the extreme strain he was under.

Thomas had been able to "fire up" his summer energy for his work, but not for his relationships. His work provided a framework that allowed for some level of familiarity that then provided security and containment so that his system could relax a little. All the while, though, entertaining and looking after so many people, his own heart was suffering until his whole system—but particularly his heart—could not go on functioning safely.

We needed to restore Thomas's *shen*.

With gentle, kind, consistent support, Thomas was able to form a few friendships that remain in his life today—something new for him. He was able to find ways of living comfortably with his conditions. He aligned himself with what his heart needed, finding ways to keep his fire settled yet gently stimulated. In his own words, he found a contentment that bordered on joy.

When massive trauma or violence (sexual or emotional in nature) occurs, the heart often dissociates itself from the event. You can go numb. However, when that immediate strategy for coping takes root, it can block your intimacy with others.

By becoming aware of what your emotions are telling you, you can keep your heart functioning at its optimum, filtering information all the time. Your aim is to disentangle yourself from the pains of your past, present, or even projected future, so that finally your feelings become an accurate barometer to guide. Until then, your feelings may be triggered by the distortions of others' perspectives—how they've treated you—which can compel you to act upon dangerous misconceptions of yourself.

Once you are switched on to the purpose of your emotional and energetic states, you can better understand the language of the clever, integrated, and ever-changing states of health within your body.

Burning the Veils

Your heart governs with an equilibrium that allows you to settle within, despite the constant paradox of life, giving you a sense of emotional stability within the constant changing ebbs and flows.

If your heart energy is clogged with layers of hurts, unexpressed emotions, and responses, then it is tricky to have your essence expressed radiantly. When your guards have been crushed with too many shocks or traumas (physical, mental, or spiritual), you are acutely and chronically vulnerable. Your heart cannot govern the internal or external domains in your life.

In real health, the heart has a way of observing what is real and what is not from a safe-guarded place. True freedom comes from realizing what is going on, rather than being limited by your superficial assessments, which are often reactive. Mastering yourself and healing your heart energy involves having the veils of illusion burnt away, layer by layer.

THE PERICARDIUM:
Battered

The role of the pericardium is to protect the heart, to act as the first line of defense against external influences. The pericardium is a double-layered sac of fibrous tissue that envelops the heart on the physical level. The space between the layers is filled with a fluid that protects the heart from external shock or trauma.

The symptoms of a pericardium imbalance (and often a heart imbalance) include:

- Agitated sleeplessness
- Frequent urination, as when suffering an infection
- A sense of slightly spinning when closing your eyes
- Lack of appetite
- A sense of lifelessness
- The inability to concentrate
- A lack of joy
- Spontaneous sweating in the hands and across the chest

Energetically, the pericardium supports the heart alongside the thermostat (triple burner), to function evenly. It guards what you call the inner and the outer frontier gates, which, quite literally and energetically, open or close according to your needs.

In general theory, the pericardium is not distinguished from the heart; instead, it is akin to the chief bodyguard, metaphorically taking down anyone or anything that threatens the sovereign ruler. With such protection, the sovereign can be truly fair and impartial— open to give and receive love, dispense justice, set boundaries, create order, resolve disputes, and fearlessly respond to the needs of all.

If the heart is unprotected, love and joy disappear, sadness and fear arise. You lose your sense of connection. You experience internal disorder. You can neither love yourself nor be open to the love of others.

When the pericardium is doing its job, it keeps out those who would do harm and allows entry to those who are trustworthy, loving, fun, and good for your fire. It deals with shocks to the systems and trauma.

Shock of any sort can have a battering effect on both the outer and inner guards to your heart energy. But the body is so clever; it has several layers of security so that it can withstand small, medium, and large shocks all the time. However, a sustained battering or a shock that devastates and penetrates your guard system is dangerous for you.

Under Siege

Under the weight of shocks, many a patient has come to me, faltering on differing levels. Instead of focusing on one, I thought I would share the overall flavor.

"I have gone totally flat," one will say. "It feels as if my whole chest area has just caved in. It's as if any protection between me and the world has gone out to lunch. There's no buffer. I am tearful, as though I've become shattered glass."

"There is nothing wrong in my present circumstances," another will confess. "In fact, I'm madly in love with an incredible man. We are getting on well, but I suddenly find myself wanting to run away and hide. I'm frightened that I'll sabotage this new relationship. He doesn't deserve that. What on earth is happening to me?"

When you are betrayed by life, love, or events, rebuilding trust—in yourself, life, or others—feels incredibly precarious. Your mind will try to control any new experience of pain and close off the gates to true intimacy, thereby keeping hurt trapped around the heart area. The energetic sledgehammer of another real love will sometimes break down all that controlled energy.

Romantic love is fraught with trauma. New love comes with risks. Few, if any, could argue this fact. Yet, living in a closed-off state will cause much more chronic damage than taking the risk involved in trusting again and then allowing intimacy to enter, layer by layer.

I have had so many people—men and women, of varying person-alities—describe, in their unique way, how the very thing they craved (love to arrive) resulted in feelings of weakness and loss of control. The overwhelming sense of vulnerability that came over them startled and shook them. Physically, their bodies were both trying to expel old sediment and protect them from more pain in the present.

My job is to uncover their previous experiences of betrayal and loss of trust so they can immediately see the connections. To help them take radical responsibility for their fire, ultimately their heart, by drawing attention to their energetic imbalance.

One Thing After the Next

One day, a farmer arrived in my clinic, sent to me by his daughter, a long-time patient. Jacob's herd of cows, valuable to him personally and financially, had to be culled when the bovine disease arrived.* This dear man had already lost his wife to cancer and his son to a hideous and freak riding accident. His daughter worried that the successive traumas had sent him over the edge to such a degree that he would never come back from it. "My father cannot take any more. He has shrunk before my eyes. Nothing used to faze him, but now he's almost gone. There's no light at all left in his eyes. He's not there anymore."

To have lost everything in such quick succession had left Jacob bereft. He was in his late sixties but looked well into his seventies (if not older). He had collapsed under the weight of the shock. The dark panda circles under his eyes exposed the lack of sleep; as he sat before me, he repeatedly clasped his hands and took shallow breaths.

"The most shocking thing is that I can no longer pray. God has always been tangible to me. It was as if He was always with me on the farm and in nature. Now, there is just this numbing void in everything. I cannot even stand up straight any longer."

Jacob admitted he was lost. When the vet had told him that the whole herd would have to be put down, he had slumped to the floor. When the time had arrived to do so, it was the last straw; Jacob had nothing left.

Our job was to rekindle Jacob's fire and regain a sense of trust in life.

With treatment, Jacob was able to transform all that had happened. He even helped other devastated farmers who had wanted to take their own lives. He had never realized that his

---

* Mad Cow Disease devastated UK farms in 2014. Thousands of herds had to be killed to stop the spread of the disease.

daughter wanted to be involved with the farm. Pulling together, they were able to build another herd.

His daughter produced two fabulous little twin girls and a boy in relatively quick succession, whom Jacob adored. His sparkle returned and he could live peacefully with the devastation of his losses.

"Do you know, Catherine, that God's grace is all around me, even more than before this terrible series of events?"

Jacob knew that he had begun to recover when his humor returned. Despite everything, humor was, perhaps, God's grace in action. "I even trust that one day I will understand what seems unfathomable to me now. Isn't it extraordinary to think that I can honor my son and wife by returning to the grace of having humor in my life every day?"

Resistance is Futile

As some aspects of your daily living are taken away through the seasons' and nature's rhythms, you often lose touch with the endless gentle reminders that everything in life is a process.

Imagine smiling joyfully, no longer resisting life, as you learn to grasp the purposes of endless changes, until one day they loosen their grip on you. What once seemed unfathomable, even untenable, suddenly appear to be the most normal of realities.

You don't have to ignore, fix, or deny what is. By acknowledging your losses and your traumas, you can be transformed to the next level. Your summer/fire energy can grow even stronger.

Returning home to your suffering can deliver you back to peace. Home is that place inside of you where you can become increasingly settled, where you accept that which must be accepted and, equally, recognize what can be changed.

I am not sure peace is a stable static state; instead, it seems more of a continuum. All of life is constant change, so peace, too, is a moving energy that gets richer for accessing what has gone before. My definition of peace: mastering the energy of daily reality, not resisting the normal moving process.

V.
Late Summer/Earth

The Season of
SYMPATHY AND CONCERN

When the stubble in the fields was burnt every year, as was the norm in my childhood, I would ride past and marvel at how nature would receive the trace minerals of ash as the plows turned over the earth.

Years later, I understood that the regular and equivalent burning I was in—recovering from one procedure after the other, one undoing after the next—was strengthening my ability to produce harvests, and establishing the next level of health and growth.

In ICM, this is the fifth season. You may be familiar with spring, summer, autumn, and winter, but late summer? It's the critical time between the seasons, where you return to the center so that you can pivot.

This transitional time belongs to the earth element as this is when the seasonally dominant energy returns to the earth to be transformed into the next seasonal energy.

Late summer conjures up fields in which abundant growth has been harvested. It is ideally a time of celebration. The harvests have been picked and collected, then transformed and transported to wherever needed. It is a time of understanding that the fields may need to be left fallow for a season to replenish the earth.

The same can be said of you. Until something is processed through and brought to the ripening stage, it will remain in your system. There is a literal kickback cycle that needs to be respected and allowed to go back before it goes forward. You generally know it as "one step forward and two back"—or "five ahead and three back." This Law of Cure is a consolidation process that needs to be worked with and through.

You can be ruled by their rottenness when you don't return these experiences to the earth. The transformation that can be had from them gets shut down.

The ripening of your life into something that expresses your skills, passions, and gifts grows out of endless layers of rotting. As you go forward, you will repeatedly find yourself in these ripening/rotting cycles that you can either go along with or get caught out by.

You can turn what's left of that harvest into the soil, making use of it, or not. The choice is always yours. The rotting and ripening of your daily life on a mind, body, and spirit level is always ready to respond to and support your actions.

The emotion connected to the late summer/earth is sympathy, also translated as worry, concern, and obsession.

When the earth energy within us is functioning at its optimum, it is compelled to lean into producing the harvest of concern, thought, and sympathy for the natural processes of life. When your energy is abundant, you can consciously choose what you do or do not do, how you respond, how you interact. That energy enables an automatic state of sympathy or concern for others.

When in balance, earth energy is impartial to what it gives birth to; it does not discern between good or bad. It is altruistic because the actions it generates carry with them no expectation of return. Earth energy also compels you to nurture in ways that, if unexpressed, can end up hurting you or those around you.

Your earth energy allows you to distinguish between when it is good to look after your own needs; and when to care for others. (My mother continually got those priorities muddled.)

Your earth is affected by your home and your mothering, nurturing connections. You can learn to mother and give birth to your own needs for continual nourishment. On the other hand, imbalanced earth energy can lead to profound misery around food, cooking, kitchen space, or just generally cherishing yourself.

An out-of-balance earth energy can be sticky and needy. It can cause those around you to feel like they're standing in quicksand. On the one hand, the energy seems to push them away; on the other, it begs to have your needs met, for some sort of sustenance—resentful martyrdom comes to mind. Until the energy is shifted in all senses and released to do what it is created to do, you will carry on this way.

Being a martyr usually leads to frayed relationships or connections, so become equally happy with saying "no" as you are with saying "yes" to requests from others. Knowing when to take care of your own needs first, instead of self-sacrificing (which is also a form of earth imbalance) is vital. Of course, vitality comes from knowing the difference between your authentic no and your resistance to people, places, or things that require you to grow through transporting and transforming.

Late summer organs include the following:

- Stomach
- Spleen

Other late summer associations that inform diagnosis:

- Element—earth
- Emotion/energy—sympathy/overthinking/worry

A *balanced* late summer energy provides the ability to:

- Ask for help; take in nurture and care when offered, not push it away
- Distinguish between when it is appropriate to look after your own needs and when to care for others
- Give support and nourishment to others

THE STOMACH:
Detached

In ICM, the stomach is your controller of rotting and ripening. It is responsible, along with the spleen, for storehouses and granaries of the body. The five tastes stem from them.

Beyond digesting food and taking in liquid, your stomach is your emotional center. The West has finally caught up with the East in this one recognition. In the English language, we have such expressions as, "I cannot stomach it," "I don't have the stomach for it," and, "It was a kick in the stomach." In other words, you experience life and its challenges through your stomach. In some senses, it is also the real hub of your mind.

Emotional disturbances crop up when there is an imbalance in the associated late summer/earth energy. How well your thought processes operate depends on how well you can "rot and ripen" the content of your life on all levels. That energy dictates how well your feedback mechanism is working, with all your feelings and emotional states being wrapped up in a whole ongoing process. Your feelings and emotions give rise to the flow of your energy system. Everything is interconnected.

Physical symptoms of a stomach disorder include:

- Swollen legs and ankles, particularly during long flights
- Perspiring on the forehead, arms, and legs

- Diarrhea after eating
- An immediate feeling of fullness when eating
- A sense of being sick most of the time
- Increasing listlessness and fatigue
- Restless sleep
- A yellowing, puffy, and damp look to the face
- An odd texture of the facial skin

What's Eating You?

When I met John, he was on his knees, having tried numerous ways of stomaching food. Severe and complex allergies were the problem, or so he believed. He lived on energy bars and protein shakes. Then John revealed that he could not trust himself to eat meals around others because he felt as though he was being judged. Although he had become obsessed with his physical appearance and was considered fit, secretly, he was very bothered by his discomfort around food, which is why he'd reached out to me. He did not know how he could date the woman he fancied if he could not and would not be able to eat with her.

When I offered him sympathy around how debilitating his allergies must be, John brushed it off as if it was nothing. The emotion of sympathy—for himself or others—was noticeably absent from his energy field.

"Do you find yourself worrying a lot, being a bit like a hamster on a treadmill, not ever really being able to let go of the constant state of worry?"

The question surprised him. First, it had described him; second, he was unsure of what it had to do with his eating issue. John's response almost sang out of his body, another clue.

When I ran through the other suspected symptoms with him, he seemed surprised that I had described his further troubles so accurately. He also appeared to be incredibly uncomfortable in his own skin.

When I took his pulses, I could tell that John was in a very extreme situation. Everything was pointing suspiciously to possible tumors and cancers—his so-called allergies were the least of his medical issues.

Without any sympathy or softness, I bluntly told him that I wanted him to go to his doctor that very day for some tests. By matching his voice and lack of sympathy, I knew I would be more settling to him. To prevent him churning away with worry, John needed to be contained by my telling him what to do and what was to happen.

After ringing his doctor, I turned to John and said, "May I suggest you do yourself a favor? For now, don't tell your mother, if that feels right to you."

He looked at me, his eyes huge with surprise. He was thirty-five years old and mortified that I might know, somehow, about the agony that the relationship with his mother still caused him.

John's mother adored him with an obsessive and excessively smothering love. She had a favorite expression that he had recounted when describing his eating issues: "No one knows the hardships of my son. He is so remarkable. It is not fair the world is so against my son. No one understands him." John had yet to unravel the effects of this broken and distorted projection, which was breaking his very capable energy. He had yet to connect his deep frustration with his mother's smothering behavior and his issues around food.

I told John precisely what to do—step-by-step—so he could let go of worrying for a bit and get himself to the hospital.

He had cancer; in fact, he needed an immediate operation.

Later, alongside dealing with his cancer—which had, unfortunately, already spread, making the necessary treatment choices—John became deeply empowered by connecting the dots of his mother's behavior.

So, without judgment, John chose to get fully behind all aspects of what had been happening to his life force.

Inevitably, John began to talk much more about his constant frustration and discomfort around his mother's smothering and very manipulative tactics. He had felt utterly caught up in the sticky treacle of being manipulated, hating himself for not knowing how to manage the dynamics productively. He began to have sympathy for his mother as well as himself. He became very conscious of boundaries around her.

It was not his mother's behavior alone that would or could be blamed for his condition; what he learned was how his actions had been contributing factors. John took full responsibility, happily becoming empowered to live very differently despite a devastating prognosis.

Fully embracing what he could and could not do to make changes and become self-nurturing, he became much more relaxed and happy. He saw all the signs and symptoms his body had been giving him as attempts to alter the frustration and unhappiness that had been his daily drivers. This, in turn, changed everything for him. John's late summer/earth energy stabilized, helping him produce his harvest from the awareness of these continual cycles of rotting and ripening.

John lived for another fifteen years, which in his own words, were the most productive and happy of his entire life. His mother also turned her life around since his stance gave her no alternative. The more he understood that he was not powerless but empowered to love his mother, though not her actions, the quicker her behavior was transformed. By not reacting, John's thriving life force extended her an invitation to drop all that was still wounding her but no longer affecting him.

Kickbacks

In ICM, there are ways of seeing the energy dynamics between a mother and her child. Words offer a very small peek inside disorders, a glimpse through the curtains.

The enormous woman who sat before me had originally brought her young son to my clinic to treat his painful stomach issues. Her child had been streaming with snot, of which she seemed to take no notice. The boy looked distressed and uncomfortable, as if in a sort of permanent cramp. She, on the other hand, radiated self-disgust. Her misery spun out all over the waiting room.

Margaret, the mother, had the energy field of someone living with very toxic shame. Likely, her vast bulk was protecting her from something that had taken place in the past. She remained stuck there—stuck in a constant rotting cycle. The experience hadn't born ripened fruit.

I needed to find a way to treat Margaret if the young boy was to avoid the "kickbacks" of her unresolved issues. Her stuck and stagnant energy was the cause of his symptoms.

Which, to make a long story short, was why she, alone, was seated before me.

I sensed what was trapped inside Margaret, so I carefully invited her to spit the "undigested and rotten" out of her. For the first time in her life, she could unpack the festering, rotting wounds that were constantly cycling and being recreated in her energy field.

She told me a group of bullies had sexually and violently abused her at the age of eleven. They had cornered her in the dark as she was walking back home. She'd been badly hurt and left for dead. A family friend found her by luck and took her home, where they rang her mother. After they had initially stabilized her, both the family friend and the mother talked through how Margaret's father (not to mention her brothers) would respond if they knew.

I let Margaret spill out as much of this festering, unspoken, and trapped story as was possible for her. Even though it was agony for her, I knew that she had not yet reached the tipping point.

It had been decided that the incident be kept secret so the father wouldn't seek revenge and wind up in prison. Love, compassion, and secrecy got all mixed in her head.

Margaret's life had only gone downhill from there.

She looked at me, trying to determine whether I could be trusted, and blurted out, "And now I'm a fat drunk. I do nothing but guzzle cakes, biscuits, anything that I can get hold of. I loathe myself. I won't even consider killing myself as I assume that I'd even cock that up."

So, Margaret was killing herself slowly; she knew because she believed she didn't deserve to be alive or have a life. "Every single day, I wake up promising myself I will stop both the sugar and the secret drinking, but then I just carry right on." She was also mean to her son behind his dad's back. Margaret had no idea why her husband hadn't left her yet when she continually pushed him away.

"I don't know how to move on or change this. Yes, I was raped, and yes, it was appalling, but the bit that I loathe and am stuck with is that it's me that keeps on violating myself with my behavior. It's as if I am poison, and now, I must continue poisoning everyone else. Is that how it has to be?"

The poison was bigger than any rational thought; it was stuck in her body, not just her mind. But I believed Margaret could recover. She needed to know she was not as alone as she felt. She didn't need to be told what she should or should not be feeling. I understood the mechanism of shame all too well.

Long after a body gets going again with so-called normal life, an energy field needs clearing. That field is like barbed wire tearing away at the stomach every day. Sharing the horrors is a part of unsticking the hold of that power. It's part of the earth-churning process.

ICM can diagnose where the roots of an issue are. The art involves finding out which layer will unravel the others. By immediately treating Margaret's spirits (her blocked energy) in her stomach, where she was still reeling from having had the earth taken from underneath her so viciously, there was now the possibility that everything else would fall back into place.

"If you want me to work with you, are you prepared for what I call the kickbacks?" I explained that each time you unlock hidden energy, you seem to get worse on some level, but only temporarily. If Margaret's spirit/life force responded to treatment, all the other physical symptoms would change along with the emotional.

And so, they did. Within six months, Margaret lost three stone (forty-two pounds). The toxic shame that was never hers in the first place fell away.

The secrets lost their hold over her. She had even been able to talk to her husband about what was really going on. She became an excellent cook, joined Alcoholics Anonymous, found her self-respect, and started loving her child and husband in ways that had not been possible before.

A byproduct of her self-compassion was her forgiveness of her rapists.

The last time I saw Margaret, she was beaming with radiance. She was unrecognizable, no longer the woman who had once sullenly entrusted me with her child.

Hurt people hurt. She was able to ripen through the rotting and stop her vicious cycle of hurting those she wanted only to love.

The Sins of the Mother

You are affected by others and cannot live in such insular ways. Everyone's life force and energy intermingle with each other's—particularly a mother's, with that of her child's. It took me many painful years to realize that it was herself that my mother could not tolerate, not me, which did not alleviate the emotional pain of her rejection. She was playing out something deeply rooted in her.

"The sins of the father are visited upon the children" implies that children often suffer for the bad things their parents do. This means, if you want your children to thrive, you must heal yourself. If you're going to heal, you may need to look to your parents and understand their experience. This is how you free yourself.

THE SPLEEN:
Contempt

The spleen converts food and drink into new cells and replenished energy. In ICM, the spleen energy is called the "transformer and transporter" of all food, drink, and substance in your body. It is responsible, along with the stomach, for the storehouses and granaries of the body.

Physical symptoms of a spleen imbalance include:

- Fatigue
- Loss of appetite
- Abdominal fullness
- Loose stools
- Breathlessness
- Sallow complexion
- Heaviness in the limbs
- Cold limbs
- Bruising
- Prolapse symptoms

Emotionally, the spleen's job is to distinguish between when it is appropriate to look after your own needs and when to care, support, and nourish others.

Energetically, many people have an open spleen, which simply means they are gifted and cursed simultaneously with being able to feel into others' emotional and energetic states. This constitutes a lack of energetic boundaries. Until they can tell the difference between what is theirs and what is not, they often carry others' unexpressed baggage, thinking it is theirs. This is empathy gone wrong—and the sign of an imbalance.

The flip side of this imbalance is contempt: a total disregard for the feelings and needs of others.

The energetic rhythms of a balanced spleen allow boundaries around the sustenance and nourishment of self and others in relation to your needs. Like the stomach, the balance of your spleen is partly set according to connections to your mother.

Spinning Gold from Straw

I could talk about many a patient, but my mother's life was a fantastic example of a spleen deficiency, an inability to transform sustenance into anything useful. I think her story dramatizes several symptoms of imbalance, which is why I will focus solely on her.

From the start, I had a fraught relationship with my mother. Yet there was much that I admired about her. She was a highly intelligent woman capable of so much of her own thinking. However, at the end of her life, she was reading The Times or The Telegraph, two British newspapers, which she took as gospel, leaving her spouting others' opinions, not her own. She wanted to focus solely on others—others not related to herself in any way. There was no harvest, no capacity to transform or replenish anything. Cancer cells spread like wildfire as there was nothing to stop them. Therefore, the transformer of all things and the trucks of supplies were all shut down.

Even before she'd taken ill, my mother's thoughts, energy, and attention had always been focused on the obsessions involved in her addictions—addictions that transformed her overriding state only momentarily. Her festering childhood wounds triggered her self-hatred.

She had the most terrible relationship with her own mother, who was almost the worst type of bully that I have ever come across—even considering the work that I have done with battered and abused spouses. My mother, when speaking of Grannie, always referred to her as "your grandmother" and never as "my mother."

My mother was constantly trying to manage the malfunctions of a body that would not have given her a moment's rest. She suffered from the same very rare connective tissue disorder that I now know has affected at least three generations of women in my family. This meant that her internal tissue matrix was struggling massively to hold together. She endured agonizing pain. All of this had to be managed somehow.

The self-hatred that drove her, which was triggered by me more than almost anyone else, was a hungry internal wolf viciously tearing at her insides; it kept her from being sympathetic to anyone except strangers. It was odd getting used to the fact that she would and could be so strangely tender, kind, hilarious, and thoughtful to almost anyone whom she did not know very well.

She was the most fantastic person to be around when she got a fit of incredibly infectious laughter; it would permeate through and around her like a bubble bath that had escaped way beyond the constraints of the tub.

I vividly remember working out that my mother did not love me but that I loved her, which I somehow realized would be my salvation. So, no matter what she did—deliberately set me up to be bullied, humiliated, or continually rejected in fantastically cruel ways—I could see through what was happening. I had no idea at the time that by doing that, I was dismantling any potential victim stance. Deep, internal knowing empowered me step-by-step, while I built up my internal energy, although it did not seem like it at the time.

Society hates a mother who deviates from the nurturing and nourishing norm. So, when a child is not being cared for, it is not out of the ordinary for that parent to manipulate the system to make it look like the child, and not she, is at fault. Not knowing how to love me, my mother had to make sure others saw me as a problem. And she did.

The more I realized how unloved and inadequate my mother felt, the more I stopped feeling so triggered; I ceased losing my temper with her in utter desperation. I even worked out that she would deliberately, though slyly, rile others to express her seething rage, misery, and confusion.

Years later, after her death, I read an account of what she knew she did to me in one of her diaries. She knew and yet was not able to stop herself; that, in and of itself, was a sick but soothing medicine for her ailments. It worked temporarily and kept her need for self-hatred going.

Shame works that way.

By getting to know my mother so well, I learned to respect and admire what she achieved. In some ways, as I managed to separate her from her behavior and her addictive personality traits from her real essence, I loved her all the more.

One of the main features of functioning spleen energy is the capacity to think with clarity. When the spleen is in balance, your capacity to think functions at its optimum. My mother did not think clearly.

But I'm happy to say, she died knowing she was loved and loveable. Her wounds and her disease had not prevented love from being what both love and nature are. At the end, she quite clearly wanted, trusted, and actively sought out my help and nurturing. She gained total focus of mind and was able to penetrate through the fog of her life and express herself in unambiguous sentences.

One day, she looked directly at me and connected to me in a way that had never been possible for her.

"Darling, are you in pain all of the time?"

"Yes, but it's something that I'm used to, and it has oddly brought me closer to the Divine in all things."

"I can see that, darling, but actually, you always were connected, even from when you were born. I was afraid of the light that shone through you. I didn't feel deserving of either of the two of you. I tried so hard to destroy you, but thank God, I never succeeded. What stuns me is that there is no bitterness anywhere in your face. I look for it; I think it should be there, but it is not. You have never stopped loving me, which I hated you for, yet now I understand. Thank you."

She died forty-eight hours later.

It is Not About Forgiveness

I am sure you'll agree that there are forces beyond your control. Often, something inherent within us must find its way through the seemingly unforgivable to the forgivable. To remember that your essence is nothing but love, which can be the ambition of a lifetime, is always your salvation. It is the only real way to transform any victim stance, as becoming loving demands that you put down your dramas and your reactivity. You learn to act and not react from the deep center that waits to be ignited within all of us.

When your self-respect and self-love expand into every corner of your being, you merely notice another's behavior; it is neither likable nor inflammatory, and you begin to know what to do. Even in the most extreme circumstances, I have seen this to be true. However, to imply that it is easy, or merely a simple Band-Aid is missing the point.

People often talk as if understanding someone or something condones behaviors. I believe that understanding the absolute truth of any situation robs it of its sometimes-detonating effects. You are set free once you can detach with loving forgiveness from another's behavior that is driven by complex webs of toxicity. By understanding what is really going on—not condoning the acts but being better prepared to deal with the truth—you can become aligned.

Conclusion

I have bumped up against the limits of the Western medical system my entire life, respecting what is to be respected and leaving the rest alone as far as is possible. Suffice it to say, it has been like walking through a minefield of fragile egos or arrogance. The paradox is that my personal experience ultimately helped me become a far better practitioner with my patients. Frustration and pain have their purposes.

After my last few surgeries, I felt wretched and bizarrely guilty like so many of my patients. Being a practitioner is a two-edged sword as people can often make remarks like, "Why can't you heal yourself?" or, "Doesn't your form of medicine work then?" (It is the marriage of two systems that has kept me alive, against such great odds.) This weird sense of having failed myself will crop up at a time when I need my own support the most. This, in turn, has also been a gift as it has released more of the neglect of my childhood. Hence, the integrated feedback mechanism within me cleverly forces another layer of unresolved frustration out of my being.

I have lost friends who hit their limits with the continual consequences of being so ill. Some have died. I have felt tribeless and lost in a new wilderness. Layer by layer, I have had to become my own best friend, first and foremost—to have the eyes, the vision of hope and kindness toward a new season and future, even in the absence of being able to "see" it.

I find again and again, season after season, that the total sense of hopelessness has turned into the treasured experience of discovering self-love in the absence of a good model. Our potential can be constantly ignited through our challenges as well.

It has been a lifelong journey to understand my mind, body, and soul to cope with these rare genetic disorders, and help others. After years of training as an ICM practitioner (because that is where my journey took me), many missing pieces came together for me. They have enabled me to find my way back to thriving and vibrant health through it all. They have given me the philosophy and the system of orientation that I've shared with you on these pages. They have given me my mission: to inspire people to thrive no matter what; to live with vitality, fun, and joy wherever it is possible.

In integrated medicine, there is no judgment, only constant assessments of individual or collective energy balance. Shame has no role in this.

Finding solutions to issues and energetic problems is not the only goal. Supporting those suffering, helping them unhook from the drama—the sense that they are victims with no control—is vital if they are to hear their own opinion, judgments, and instincts.

The Purpose

Life is often presented to us as a series of endless, quick, external fixes. Surely, though, one of the amazing honors of your life is transforming your journey into something that keeps taking you home to yourself. To keep believing the powerfully peddled illusions of sickness and the need for fixing is dangerous; by doing so, you delay the mastering of yourself. Pain is natural, cyclical, purposeful.

It is the greatest alarm system you have. It is not there to be fixed or white-washed or run from.

By going through pain, you become who you are meant to become.

You must live alongside pain. Nature demands it. You must connect with yourself and harness all the rot that invariably happens to strengthen, not dwindle, your internal resources. You can thrive, not just despite emotional and physical suffering, but because of it.

But first, you must connect to the language of your mind, body, and essence (spirit) so that you can enjoy energetic integrated health despite (or because of) your difficult reality.

No wonder nearly every religion and philosophy throughout the ages has taught that to "know yourself is of the utmost importance." If you can tune in to what's happening inside of you and pinpoint the source of energetic imbalance and discomfort, you can understand how that affects everything else.

But to get at any of that, you need to know yourself, and in this noisy world, that takes some doing.

Connection

The more connected you are to your truth and the more you have made it a priority to know yourself, the more present and available you are to others, as well as the world. You start living connected to your world, rather than disconnected, isolated, and cut off from the never-ending consequences of your actions and those of others.

Chinese medicine sees the human body as interrelated and connected to the environment. You are affected by others and cannot live in such insular ways. Everyone's life force and energy intermingle with each other's.

This means:

- You interact with everything and everyone around you, for good or bad.
- Dis-ease is situated in the context of a person's life and history.
- Often, a physical manifestation is indicative of a relational issue in your life. The physical imbalance aggravates the relationship imbalance, and a cycle is set.
- Waking up to some of your unpleasant behaviors, traits, and patterns can be enormously liberating and healing.
- Understanding that the health of your organs can be affected by your behaviors, and vice versa, not simply by medicine (or nutrition).

Most Western societies have a dangerous notion of independence and individuality. Friends and family influence outcomes up to a point, we like to think, but not those beyond our immediate circle, and certainly not those of previous generations. The connection between your individual choices and actions, and their consequences in the broader collective, is not yet a part of our general consciousness. (Global warming did not come out of nowhere.) Yet, these are part of the accounting in integrated medicine.

The Chinese have a traditional understanding that what (or who) they are and do is always a result of what has gone before them; how they behave always defines how the next generations will be affected. In the West, we might say, "The sins of the father are visited upon the children," which implies that children often suffer for the things their parents do. Until epigenetics, the study of heritable changes in gene expression, this is the closest we've had to an understanding of this collective concept. You may get nature versus nurture, but not the *genetic* transfer of experiences, feelings, or beliefs.

Yet, you may carry a vague sense of guilt that has been passed down through the generations, which unknowingly continues to influence your behaviors and choices. You are not yet fully aware of where your thoughts or beliefs come from; they may well be inherited. These must be challenged, particularly when you're out of balance.

There are also many external reasons why you may be out of balance.

The Five Seasons Revisited

ICM teaches that humans should live in harmony with the five seasons. Each season has many associations that help change your habits, allowing for a more balanced mind and body.

Each season has a corresponding element. Everyone is a blend of these elements, and to be truly healthy, they need to be balanced. Each element has an associated emotion, and a form of depression. These emotions are influenced by particular organs, with their own associated energy. These energy systems can get blocked and imbalanced. Disease and pain indicate a blockage; they serve as a feedback mechanism that can be read. Every single aspect of how you present yourself each day is a loud statement of the state of your organs.

Most dis-ease is about one or more of your internal accounts being over- or underspent. Your energy—that of your body, mind, and spirit—has its own spreadsheet, which is influenced by any number of things based on your past, present, and future. The depletion of your resources leads to anxiety and other long-term unresolved emotional problems and the literal burning up of your internal and external energy resources. These energetic imbalances can be accounted for in a myriad of ways. The resultant dis-ease that presents is often surprising, as the stories of my patients demonstrate.

If you have an internal imbalance or stagnation, it may not only disturb your health but also radiate out, starting with how you show up in the world; which then impacts your relationships; which in turn upsets your social network or ecosystem; which impacts society; then spreads to the natural world, the planet. And vice versa.

So within, so without. That is one of the most critical lessons in this book. Which takes us right back to the beginning of the cycle.

The Seasonal Dance

Life is a constant paradox. Seasonal weather is part of our lives and not something we should try to skirt. To attempt to do so will not serve us but hinder what we are meant to be or do. This is another vital lesson.

No matter how harsh, every season affords you an opportunity to become more familiar with all aspects of yourself in an integrated and interconnected way.

It is normal to go through levels of dis-ease, cycles of health followed by pain, just like the seasons. It is the human condition. When you understand this, you can set your spirit free. Your purpose can come to light as your self-love and self-respect increase. You can see and know your body and its organs in ways that you never imagined possible; treat them like the alarm systems they are.

Your systems are there to serve you. The next time you are quick to condemn a symptom or a state of dis-ease, see if you can first make sure that there isn't a deeper subtext that needs to be released, witnessed, and healed. You have layers to release. This you must do despite the "fix it" energy running the world at present, selling the idea that you're faulty goods in need of so much more before it's possible to thrive. Your unique potential is longing to thrive through all the inevitable challenges that are a normal part of life. As a collective feedback mechanism, your mental, physical, and emotional body is already okay.

The goal is to get to the roots of dis-ease: unravel the layers of your potential and come to terms with the layers of dis-ease that are collectively shared—because we're all human, complete with contrasts, contradictions, and conflicting emotions. The goal is also to see the interconnection of every single aspect of living, breathing, eating, and behaving—within us and without.

Ultimately, you must discover and unravel who you really are.

Treat your own body like you would a new love affair. Be diligent, careful, and thorough, taking nothing for granted. If you want a great lover and companion, it is worth the wait and patience involved to work out if that person is right for you. In the same way, get to know your body.

Always and in all ways, ask yourself whether a state of dis-ease has roots in your mind, body, or spirit. Use your time to be a friend to your body, mind, and spirit, knowing that it is the marriage of this combination that gives you strength.

When your self-respect and self-love expand into every single corner of your being, you will notice that another's behavior is not likable or inflammatory; and you will know what to do in response. You'll begin to see. Even in the most extreme circumstances. Loving action—and your energy systems—will find ways to interact with the reality of others; you will remain detached and yet connected to them. The time will come when you are less affected by them, when you can influence them just by your energy systems and their natural rhythms.

Let me leave you with this final thought: Every single function of your mind, body, and spirit operates as one. The more you understand these functions, the more you can influence your life. I call this influence my silver thread. You must fully embrace how integrated everything is. You so often ignore the inevitable boomerang effect, which, sooner or later, is the obvious consequence of all of your actions. Through evolving, though, you can begin to take what I call radical responsibility for all of your life—not only some of it.

You were designed to be at peace and be happy, and not just because everything is like a chocolate box fantasy in your ever-changing life. You are in a win/win situation and can place your trust in the perpetual balancing act of the natural world. You can exert a significant influence. You can go from being tossed about in some terrifying sea to thriving and living with expanding levels of choice. You have the power to choose your response to the events, people, places, and things around you. You work *with* an amazing mind, body, and spirit, not against insurmountable obstacles.

Pain is not your enemy; there is no need to run. Pain is merely part of your experience, something that you are fully equipped to deal with. You will not avoid pain in life, but suffering can become optional.

Acknowledgements

I'd very much like to thank Andrew Baker who has been remarkable in his steadfastness, loyalty, and seemingly unshakeable belief in me and the bigger picture. Most folks would have run away, given the demanding days and the multiple medical events I've experienced, but not you. You not only provide me shelter in the storms, but laughter at the most crucial times.

Toby, my remarkably kind, thoughtful, and talented brother, you live with a fierce courage in the paradox of pain. You continue to teach me generosity of soul. Thank you.

To my incredible friends, Sarah White, Bonnie Rowland, Di Cox, Stella Welton, and Jessica Gill. You make my days glorious, and not just because we share a sense of the absurd. Thank you for encouraging me daily, if not in person, then across the airwaves. You are all as close to being my Maverick Angels as I can imagine, at least on this plain. Without your support I would not have become the gutsy woman that I am today.

Three other women need to be mentioned for their wonderfully loving and encouraging brilliance, not to mention their expertise in birthing the bigger concept behind this book. I'm talking to you, Fabienne Tyler, Liz Turtle, and Alexandra Sagarra. Thank you for all you do.

Caroline Wimmers, you were the lightning rod that also introduced me to Ann. I shall forever be grateful. One day we will celebrate together.

Ann Sheybani, thank you for being the most fantastic book midwife that anyone could have. Your editing skills and mother goosing have taken this book to amazing levels. You have a razor-sharp brain loaded with wit. It has been a pleasure and an honor to have my work in your hands. I have honestly loved the time spent with you.

Recommended Reading

Blyth, Danny, and Greg Lampert. *Chinese Dietary Wisdom: Eating for Health and Wellbeing*. Nutshell Press, 2019. Kindle.

- A fantastic book to help you to treasure your spleen with food.

Cabot, Sandra. *Heal Your Gut: An A to Z Guide: Healthy Bowel Healthy Body*. Phoenix, AZ: SCB International Inc., 2014.

Cabot, Sandra. *The Healthy Liver & Bowel Book: Detoxification Strategies for Your Liver & Bowel*. Phoenix, AZ: SCB International Inc., 2006.

- Keeping your liver clean will dramatically affect your thoughts, moods, and behaviors. I have used the two books listed here (by Dr. Sandra Cabot) extensively over the years—both are well worth looking into.
- Sandra Cabot's liver cleanse can also help immensely with gallbladder issues.

Hafiz, and Daniel Ladinsky. *I Heard God Laughing: Poems of Hope and Joy*. New York: Penguin Books, 2006.

Hicks, Angela, and John Hicks. *Healing Your Emotions: Discover Your Five Element Type and Change Your Life*. London: HarperThorsons, 2017.

- More information on your seasons; it also contains practical exercises.

James, John W., and Russell Friedman et al. *When Children Grieve: For Adults to Help Children Deal with Death, Divorce, Pet Loss, Moving, and Other Losses*. New York: Harper Perennial, 2002.

- This is an incredible source of information and guidance to help you retrace your own earlier life.

McLelland, Jane. *How To Starve Cancer*. Agenor Publishing, 2018.

McTaggart, Lynn. *The Intention Experiment*. New York: Atria Books, 2008.

- A fascinating read. McTaggart refers to herself as "a hard-nosed journalist who did not believe in anything but hard-core facts and science."

Mindell, Earl. *Vitamin Bible: Over 200 Vitamins and Supplements for Improving Health, Wellness, and Longevity*. New York: Grand Central Publishing, 2021.

Mosley, Michael. *The Clever Gut Diet: How to Revolutionize Your Body from the Inside Out*. New York: Atria Books, 2018.

- A great (and correct) quote from Dr. Mosley's book: "Your bedroom is for rest, sleep, and sex. Nothing else."

Osho. *The Tantra Experience: Evolution Through Love: On the Royal Song of Saraha*. New York: Osho Media International, 2012.

- A glorious book that may be a soothing night-time look-through.

Pomroy, Haylie. *The Burn: Why Your Scale is Stuck and What to Eat About It*. New York: Harmony Books, 2014.

- I love this book because there are three manageable sections, each packed with valuable information. The chapter on digestion is excellent in connection with this season.

Ponder, Catherin. *The Dynamic Laws of Prayer*. Camarillo, CA: De Vorss, 1987.

- A clever exploration of the power behind prayer.

Ross, Julia. *The Mood Cure: The 4-Step Program to Rebalance Your Emotional Chemistry and Rediscover Your Natural Sense of Well-Being*. New York: Penguin Life, 2003.

- If you recognize that you have problems with depression or suffer from moods that keep altering, this is a useful book.

Rowland, David. *Nutritional Solutions for 88 Conditions.* Bloomington, IN: Balboa Press, 2016.

Rowland, David. *What Your Body Is Telling You: And What You Can Do About It.* Bloomington, IN: Balboa Press, 2017.

- David Rowland is Canada's foremost expert in holistic nutrition. He published Nutritiapedia®, the free online nutritional encyclopedia; and created the Nutri-body® system, which natural health practitioners use to determine nutritional and biochemical weaknesses. He is an extraordinary fountain of knowledge—fully utilizing his brain the size of the cosmos for the sake of humanity.

Sabbage, Sophie. *The Cancer Whisperer.* London: Coronet, 2019.

Sabbage, Sophie. *Lifeshocks.* London: Coronet, 2019.

Savory, Barrie. *The Good Back Guide.* London: Century, 2006.

- This book by Barrie Savory, DO, is worth having on your bookshelf, as it is full of critical integrated information about your structure.

Savory, Barrie. *The Good Back Guide.* London: Century, 2006.

- Barrie Savory has been my osteopath since my early teens. His book is beautifully written—and written by a man who is still passionate about his work and the human body.

Summers, Patty. *Talking with the Animals*. Newburyport, MA: Hampton Roads Publishing, 1998.

- A fabulous book written by an animal whisperer.

Winters, Nasha, and Jess Higgins Kelley. *The Metabolic Approach to Cancer*. White River Junction, VT: Chelsea Green Publishing, 2017.

Additional Resources

Here are a few things I encourage you to look up…

- Carole Henderson's The Grief Recovery Method® in the UK or The Grief Recovery® Institute in the USA.
- Caroline Myss and her work on archetypes.
- MindUP™ | The Goldie Hawn Foundation, to learn about the incredible work they are doing for our next generations.
- Michael S. Tyrrell's Wholetones™ CDs. His Healing Frequency Music Project is a powerful tool in healing the energy tangles in your earth and other areas.

About Those Syndromes

The following are brief descriptions of the three primary syndromes by which I've been challenged:

Ehlers-Danlos syndrome (EDS) is a group of genetic tissue disorders. Although signs vary hugely according to what type of EDS the person has, typically, the joints, skin, and blood vessels are affected; effects range from mildly loose joints to life-threatening complications.

Musculoskeletal symptoms include hypermobile joints that are unstable and prone to sprain, dislocation, subluxation, and hyperextension. There can be an early onset of advanced osteoarthritis, chronic degenerative joint disease, swan-neck deformity of the fingers, and boutonniere deformity of the fingers. Tearing of tendons or muscles may occur. Deformities of the spine, such as scoliosis (curvature of the spine), kyphosis (a thoracic hump), tethered spinal cord syndrome, and occipitoatlantoaxial hypermobility may also be present. There can also be myalgia (muscle pain) and arthralgia (joint pain), which may be severe and disabling. Trendelenburg's sign is often seen—this means that when standing on one leg, the pelvis drops on the other side. Osgood–Schlatter disease, a painful lump on the knee, is also common. Walking can be delayed (beyond eighteen months of age) in infants, and bottom-shuffling instead of crawling occurs.

Mast cell activation syndrome (MCAS) is one type of mast cell activation disorder (MCAD). It is an immunological condition in which mast cells inappropriately and excessively release chemical mediators, resulting in a range of chronic symptoms, including anaphylaxis or near-anaphylaxis attacks. Primary symptoms include cardiovascular, dermatological, gastrointestinal, neurological, and respiratory problems.

MCAS remains a poorly understood condition and is a current topic of research. It is often found in patients with Ehlers–Danlos syndrome (EDS) and postural orthostatic tachycardia syndrome (POTS). It is also found in subset groups of patients with common variable immunodeficiency (CVID).

Postural orthostatic tachycardia syndrome (POTS) is a condition in which a change from lying to standing causes a significant increase in heart rate, with a startling drop in blood pressure. This occurs with symptoms that may include light-headedness, trouble thinking, blurry vision, or weakness.

**When my blood pressure drops, I struggle to form sentences—which makes people comment on how "articulate" I am. A joke!

About the Author

Catherine Rolt is an Integrated Chinese
Medical Consultant and Grief Recovery
Specialist who offers compassion and help
with all forms of physical and/or emotional
pain. She understands chronic ailments not
just on a professional level, but on a personal
one as well. Born with rare diseases, she is
a thriving example of resilience, surrender,
and self-empowerment. Her mission is to help those living with
chronic conditions experience far more hope and joy.

Catherine lives and works in West Sussex and London. She runs
an online membership for those who can't travel for treatment.

She can be reached at info@unraveldis-easenaturally.com.

Photograph by Robin Feild: www.impromptuphotography.co.uk.

Get Your Free Assessment!

Thank you for reading *The Pain Paradox: How Pain Can Lead to Inner Peace and Lightness of Being* where you found insights and strategies people just like you have used to first understand then eliminate chronic pain. As an additional thank you for reading this book, I've created a special assessment you can take that couldn't be included in this book.

- Have you struggled with emotional or physical pain?
- Have you found little relief even though you've followed doctors' orders?

If so, **you may have a seasonal energetic imbalance that is blocking you from feeling better.** Discover what's blocking you from the relief you want. The assessment will allow us to identify where you have balancing work to do. Go HERE now:

Unraveldis-easenaturally.com/quiz

And join our Free Online Community!

If you're interested in relieving chronic pain visit us at: **Unraveldis-easenaturally.com** Share your experiences and challenges as you create a pain free life. And remember, pain has a lot to teach you. It tells you when you need to address something vital in your life, like your relationships.

Printed in Great Britain
by Amazon